ELEMENTS OF THE THEORY OF FUNCTIONS

AND FUNCTIONAL ANALYSIS

VOLUME 2

MEASURE. THE LEBESGUE INTEGRAL. HILBERT SPACE

OTHER *GRAYLOCK* PUBLICATIONS

Elements of the Theory of Functions and Functional Analysis

VOLUME 2

MEASURE. THE LEBESGUE INTEGRAL. HILBERT SPACE

BY

A. N. KOLMOGOROV AND S. V. FOMIN

TRANSLATED FROM THE FIRST (1960) RUSSIAN EDITION
by
HYMAN KAMEL AND HORACE KOMM

Department of Mathematics
Rensselaer Polytechnic Institute

GRAYLOCK PRESS
ALBANY, N. Y.
1961

Library of Congress Catalog Card Number 57-4134

Manufactured in the United States of America

CONTENTS

CHAPTER V

MEASURE THEORY

CHAPTER VI

MEASURABLE FUNCTIONS

CHAPTER VII

THE LEBESGUE INTEGRAL

CHAPTER VIII

SQUARE INTEGRABLE FUNCTIONS

CHAPTER IX

ABSTRACT HILBERT SPACE. INTEGRAL EQUATIONS WITH SYMMETRIC KERNEL

PREFACE

This book is the second volume of *Elements of the Theory of Functions and Functional Analysis* (the first volume was *Metric and Normed Spaces*, Graylock Press, 1957). Most of the second volume is devoted to an exposition of measure theory and the Lebesgue integral. These concepts, particularly the concept of measure, are discussed with some degree of generality. However, in order to achieve greater intuitive insight, we begin with the definition of plane Lebesgue measure. The reader who wishes to do so may, after reading §33, go on at once to Ch. VI and then to the Lebesgue integral, if he understands the measure relative to which this integral is taken to be the usual linear or plane Lebesgue measure.

The exposition of measure theory and the Lebesgue integral in this volume is based on the lectures given for many years by A. N. Kolmogorov in the Department of Mathematics and Mechanics at the University of Moscow. The final draft of the text of this volume was prepared for publication by S. V. Fomin.

The content of Volumes 1 and 2 is approximately that of the course Analysis III given by A. N. Komogorov for students in the Department of Mathematics.

For convenience in cross-reference, the numbering of chapters and sections in the second volume is a continuation of that in the first.

Corrections to Volume 1 have been listed in a supplement at the end of Volume 2.

A. N. KOLMOGOROV
S. V. FOMIN

January 1958

TRANSLATORS' NOTE

In order to enhance the usefulness of this book as a text, a complete set of exercises (listed at the end of each section) has been prepared by H. Kamel. It is hoped that the exercises will not only test the reader's understanding of the text, but will also introduce or extend certain topics which were either not mentioned or briefly alluded to in the original.

The material which appeared in the original in small print has been enclosed by stars (★) in this translation.

Chapter V
MEASURE THEORY

The measure $\mu(A)$ of a set A is a natural generalization of the following concepts:

1) The length $l(\Delta)$ of a segment Δ.

2) The area $S(F)$ of a plane figure F.

3) The volume $V(G)$ of a three-dimensional figure G.

4) The increment $\varphi(b) - \varphi(a)$ of a nondecreasing function $\varphi(t)$ on a half-open interval $[a, b)$.

5) The integral of a nonnegative function over a one-, two-, or three-dimensional region, etc.

The concept of the measure of a set, which originated in the theory of functions of a real variable, has subsequently found numerous applications in the theory of probability, the theory of dynamical systems, functional analysis and other branches of mathematics.

In §33 we discuss the concept of measure for plane sets, based on the area of a rectangle. The general theory of measure is taken up in §§35–39. The reader will easily notice, however, that all the arguments and results of §33 are general in character and are repeated with no essential changes in the abstract theory.

§33. The measure of plane sets

We consider the collection $\mathfrak{S}$ of sets in the plane (x, y), each of which is defined by an inequality of the form

$$a \leq x \leq b,$$
$$a < x \leq b,$$
$$a \leq x < b,$$
$$a < x < b,$$

and by an inequality of the form

$$c \leq y \leq d,$$
$$c < y \leq d,$$
$$c \leq y < d,$$
$$c < y < d,$$

1

where a, b, c and d are arbitrary real numbers. We call the sets of $\mathfrak{S}$ *rectangles*. A closed rectangle defined by the inequalities

$$a \leq x \leq b; \quad c \leq y \leq d$$

is a rectangle in the usual sense (together with its boundary) if $a < b$ and $c < d$, or a segment (if $a = b$ and $c < d$ or $a < b$ and $c = d$), or a point (if $a = b$, $c = d$), or, finally, the empty set (if $a > b$ or $c > d$). An open rectangle

$$a < x < b; \quad c < y < d$$

is a rectangle without its boundary or the empty set, depending on the relative magnitudes of a, b, c and d. Each of the rectangles of the remaining types (we shall call them half-open rectangles) is either a proper rectangle with one, two or three sides included, or an interval, or a half-interval, or, finally, the empty set.

The measure of a rectangle is defined by means of its area from elementary geometry as follows:

a) The measure of the empty set $\emptyset$ is zero.

b) The measure of a nonempty rectangle (closed, open or half-open), defined by the numbers a, b, c and d, is equal to

$$(b - a)(d - c).$$

Hence, we have assigned to each rectangle P a number $m(P)$—the measure of P. The following conditions are obviously satisfied:

1) The measure $m(P)$ is real-valued and nonnegative.

2) The measure $m(P)$ is additive, i.e., if $P = \bigcup_{k=1}^{n} P_k$ and $P_i \cap P_k = \emptyset$ for $i \neq k$, then

$$m(P) = \sum_{k=1}^{n} m(P_k).$$

Our problem is to extend the measure $m(P)$, defined above for rectangles, to a more general class of sets, while retaining Properties 1) and 2).

The first step consists in extending the concept of measure to the so called elementary sets. We shall call a plane set *elementary* if it can be written, in at least one way, as a union of a finite number of pairwise disjoint rectangles.

In the sequel we shall need

THEOREM 1. *The union, intersection, difference and symmetric difference of two elementary sets is an elementary set.*

Proof. It is clear that the intersection of two rectangles is again a rectangle. Therefore, if

$$A = \bigcup_k P_k, \quad B = \bigcup_j Q_j$$

are elementary sets, then

$$A \cap B = \bigcup_{k,j} (P_k \cap Q_j)$$

is also an elementary set.

It is easily verified that the difference of two rectangles is an elementary set. Consequently, subtraction of an elementary set from a rectangle yields an elementary set (as the intersection of elementary sets). Now let A and B be two elementary sets. There is clearly a rectangle P containing both sets. Then

$$A \cup B = P \setminus [(P \setminus A) \cap (P \setminus B)]$$

is an elementary set. Since

$$A \setminus B = A \cap (P \setminus B),$$
$$A \bigtriangleup B = (A \cup B) \setminus (A \cap B),$$

it follows that the difference and the symmetric difference of two elementary sets are elementary sets. This proves the theorem.

We now define the measure $m'(A)$ of an elementary set A as follows: If

$$A = \bigcup_k P_k,$$

where the P_k are pairwise disjoint rectangles, then

$$m'(A) = \sum_k m(P_k).$$

We shall prove that $m'(A)$ is independent of the way in which A is represented as a union of rectangles. Let

$$A = \bigcup_k P_k = \bigcup_j Q_j,$$

where P_k and Q_j are rectangles, and $P_i \cap P_k = \emptyset$, $Q_i \cap Q_k = \emptyset$ for $i \neq k$. Since $P_k \cap Q_j$ is a rectangle, in virtue of the additivity of the measure for rectangles we have

$$\sum_k m(P_k) = \sum_{k,j} m(P_k \cap Q_j) = \sum_j m(Q_j).$$

It is easily seen that the measure of elementary sets defined in this way is nonnegative and additive.

A property of the measure of elementary sets important for the sequel is given by

THEOREM 2. *If A is an elementary set and $\{A_n\}$ is a countable (finite or denumerable) collection of elementary sets such that*

$$A \subseteq \bigcup_n A_n,$$

then

(1) $$m'(A) \leq \sum_n m'(A_n).$$

Proof. For arbitrary $\epsilon > 0$ and given A there obviously exists a closed elementary set $\bar{A}$ contained in A and satisfying the condition

$$m'(\bar{A}) \geq m'(A) - \epsilon/2.$$

[It is sufficient to replace each of the k rectangles P_i whose union is A by a closed rectangle contained in P_i and having an area greater than $m(P_i) - \epsilon/2^{k+1}$.]

Furthermore, for each n there is an open elementary set $\tilde{A}_n$ containing A_n and such that

$$m'(\tilde{A}_n) \leq m'(A_n) + \epsilon/2^{n+1}.$$

It is clear that

$$\bar{A} \subseteq \bigcup_n \tilde{A}_n .$$

Since $\bar{A}$ is compact, by the Heine-Borel theorem (see §18, Theorem 4) $\{\tilde{A}_n\}$ contains a finite subsequence $\tilde{A}_{n_1}, \cdots, \tilde{A}_{n_s}$ which covers $\bar{A}$. Obviously,

$$m'(\bar{A}) \leq \sum_{i=1}^{s} m'(\tilde{A}_{n_i}).$$

[In the contrary case $\bar{A}$ would be covered by a finite number of rectangles the sum of whose areas is less than $m'(\bar{A})$, which is clearly impossible.] Therefore,

$$\begin{aligned}
m'(A) \leq m'(\bar{A}) + \epsilon/2 &\leq \sum_{i=1}^{s} m'(\tilde{A}_{n_i}) + \epsilon/2 \\
&\leq \sum_n m'(\tilde{A}_n) + \epsilon/2 \\
&\leq \sum_n m'(A_n) + \sum_n \epsilon/2^{n+1} + \epsilon/2 \\
&= \sum_n m'(A_n) + \epsilon.
\end{aligned}$$

Since $\epsilon > 0$ is arbitrary, (1) follows.

The class of elementary sets does not exhaust all the sets considered in elementary geometry and classical analysis. It is therefore natural to pose the question of extending the concept of measure, while retaining its fundamental properties, to a class of sets wider than the finite unions of rectangles with sides parallel to the coordinate axes.

This problem was solved, in a certain sense definitively, by Lebesgue in the early years of the twentieth century.

In presenting the Lebesgue theory of measure it will be necessary to consider not only finite, but also infinite unions of rectangles.

In order to avoid infinite values of the measure, we restrict ourselves in the sequel to sets contained in the square $E = \{0 \leq x \leq 1; 0 \leq y \leq 1\}$.

We define two functions, $\mu^*(A)$ and $\mu_*(A)$, on the class of all sets A contained in E.

DEFINITION 1. *The outer measure $\mu^*(A)$ of a set A is*

$$\mu^*(A) = \inf \left\{ \sum m(P_k); A \subset \bigcup P_k \right\},$$

where the lower bound is taken over all coverings of A by countable collections of rectangles.

DEFINITION 2. *The inner measure $\mu_*(A)$ of a set A is*

$$\mu_*(A) = 1 - \mu^*(E \setminus A).$$

It is easy to see that

$$\mu_*(A) \leq \mu^*(A)$$

for every set A.

For, suppose that there is a set $A \subset E$ such that

$$\mu_*(A) > \mu^*(A),$$

i.e.,

$$\mu^*(A) + \mu^*(E \setminus A) < 1.$$

Then there exist sets of rectangles $\{P_i\}$ and $\{Q_k\}$ covering A and $E \setminus A$, respectively, such that

$$\sum_i m(P_i) + \sum_k m(Q_k) < 1.$$

Denoting the union of the sets $\{P_i\}$ and $\{Q_k\}$ by $\{R_j\}$, we see that

$$E \subseteq \bigcup_j R_j, \qquad m(E) > \sum_j m(R_j).$$

This contradicts Theorem 2.

DEFINITION 3. *A set A is said to be measurable (in the sense of Lebesgue) if*

$$\mu_*(A) = \mu^*(A).$$

The common value $\mu(A)$ of the outer and inner measures of a measurable set A is called its Lebesgue measure.

We shall derive the fundamental properties of Lebesgue measure and measurable sets, but first we prove the following property of outer measure.

THEOREM 3. *If*

$$A \subseteq \bigcup_n A_n,$$

where $\{A_n\}$ is a countable collection of sets, then

$$\mu^*(A) \leq \sum_n \mu^*(A_n).$$

Proof. According to the definition of outer measure, for each n and every

$\epsilon > 0$ there is a countable collection of rectangles $\{P_{nk}\}$ such that $A_n \subseteq \bigcup_k P_{nk}$ and

$$\sum_k m(P_{nk}) \leq \mu^*(A_n) + \epsilon/2^n.$$

Then

$$A \subseteq \bigcup_n \bigcup_k P_{nk},$$

and

$$\mu^*(A) \leq \sum_n \sum_k m(P_{nk}) \leq \sum_n \mu^*(A_n) + \epsilon.$$

This completes the proof of the theorem.

Theorem 4 below shows that the measure m' introduced for elementary sets coincides with the Lebesgue measure of such sets.

THEOREM 4. *Every elementary set A is measurable, and $\mu(A) = m'(A)$.*

Proof. If A is an elementary set and $P_1, \cdots, P_k$ are rectangles whose union is A, then by definition

$$m'(A) = \sum_{i=1}^{k} m(P_i).$$

Since the rectangles P_i cover A,

$$\mu^*(A) \leq \sum_i m(P_i) = m'(A).$$

But if $\{Q_j\}$ is an arbitrary countable set of rectangles covering A, then, by Theorem 2, $m'(A) \leq \sum_j m(Q_j)$. Consequently, $m'(A) \leq \mu^*(A)$. Hence, $m'(A) = \mu^*(A)$.

Since $E \setminus A$ is also an elementary set, $m'(E \setminus A) = \mu^*(E \setminus A)$. But

$$m'(E \setminus A) = 1 - m'(A), \qquad \mu^*(E \setminus A) = 1 - \mu_*(A).$$

Hence,

$$m'(A) = \mu_*(A).$$

Therefore,

$$m'(A) = \mu^*(A) = \mu_*(A) = \mu(A).$$

Theorem 4 implies that Theorem 2 is a special case of Theorem 3.

THEOREM 5. *In order that a set A be measurable it is necessary and sufficient that it have the following property: for every $\epsilon > 0$ there exists an elementary set B such that*

$$\mu^*(A \triangle B) < \epsilon.$$

In other words, the measurable sets are precisely those which can be approximated to an arbitrary degree of accuracy by elementary sets. For the proof of Theorem 5 we require the following

Lemma. *For arbitrary sets A and B,*

$$| \mu^*(A) - \mu^*(B) | \leq \mu^*(A \Delta B).$$

Proof of the Lemma. Since

$$A \subset B \cup (A \Delta B),$$

it follows that

$$\mu^*(A) \leq \mu^*(B) + \mu^*(A \Delta B).$$

Hence the lemma follows if $\mu^*(A) \geq \mu^*(B)$. If $\mu^*(A) \leq \mu^*(B)$, the lemma follows from the inequality

$$\mu^*(B) \leq \mu^*(A) + \mu^*(A \Delta B),$$

which is proved in the same way as the inequality above.

Proof of Theorem 5.

Sufficiency. Suppose that for arbitrary $\epsilon > 0$ there exists an elementary set B such that

$$\mu^*(A \Delta B) < \epsilon.$$

Then, according to the Lemma,

(1) $$| \mu^*(A) - m'(B) | = | \mu^*(A) - \mu^*(B) | < \epsilon.$$

In the same way, since

$$(E \smallsetminus A) \Delta (E \smallsetminus B) = A \Delta B,$$

it follows that

(2) $$| \mu^*(E \smallsetminus A) - m'(E \smallsetminus B) | < \epsilon.$$

Inequalities (1) and (2) and

$$m'(B) + m'(E \smallsetminus B) = m'(E) = 1$$

imply that

$$| \mu^*(A) + \mu^*(E \smallsetminus A) - 1 | < 2\epsilon.$$

Since $\epsilon > 0$ is arbitrary,

$$\mu^*(A) + \mu^*(E \smallsetminus A) = 1,$$

and the set A is measurable.

Necessity. Suppose that A is measurable, i.e.,

$$\mu^*(A) + \mu^*(E \smallsetminus A) = 1.$$

For arbitrary $\epsilon > 0$ there exist sets of rectangles $\{B_n\}$ and $\{C_n\}$ such that

$$A \subseteq \bigcup_n B_n , \qquad E \setminus A \subseteq \bigcup_n C_n$$

and such that

$$\sum_n m(B_n) \leq \mu^*(A) + \epsilon/3, \qquad \sum_n m(C_n) \leq \mu^*(E \setminus A) + \epsilon/3.$$

Since $\sum_n m(B_n) < \infty$, there is an N such that

$$\sum_{n>N} m(B_n) < \epsilon/3;$$

set

$$B = \sum_{n=1}^{n=N} B_n .$$

It is clear that the set

$$P = \bigcup_{n>N} B_n$$

contains $A \setminus B$, while the set

$$Q = \bigcup_n (B \cap C_n)$$

contains $B \setminus A$. Consequently, $A \vartriangle B \subseteq P \cup Q$. Also

$$\mu^*(P) \leq \sum_{n>N} m(B_n) < \epsilon/3.$$

Let us estimate $\mu^*(Q)$. To this end, we note that

$$(\bigcup_n B_n) \cup (\bigcup_n (C_n \setminus B)) = E,$$

and consequently

(3) $$\sum_n m(B_n) + \sum_n m'(C_n \setminus B) \geq 1.$$

But, by hypothesis,

(4)
$$\sum_n m(B_n) + \sum_n m(C_n) \leq \mu^*(A) + \mu^*(E \setminus A) + 2\epsilon/3$$
$$= 1 + 2\epsilon/3.$$

From (3) and (4) we obtain

$$\sum_n m(C_n) - \sum_n m'(C_n \setminus B) = \sum_n m'(C_n \cap B) < 2\epsilon/3,$$

i.e.,

$$\mu^*(Q) < 2\epsilon/3.$$

Therefore,

$$\mu^*(A \vartriangle B) \leq \mu^*(P) + \mu^*(Q) < \epsilon.$$

Hence, if A is measurable, for every $\epsilon > 0$ there exists an elementary set B such that $\mu^*(A \vartriangle B) < \epsilon$. This proves Theorem 5.

THEOREM 6. *The union and intersection of a finite number of measurable sets are measurable sets.*

Proof. It is clearly enough to prove the assertion for two sets. Suppose that A_1 and A_2 are measurable sets. Then for arbitrary $\epsilon > 0$ there are elementary sets B_1 and B_2 such that

$$\mu^*(A_1 \vartriangle B_1) < \epsilon/2, \qquad \mu^*(A_2 \vartriangle B_2) < \epsilon/2.$$

Since

$$(A_1 \cup A_2) \vartriangle (B_1 \cup B_2) \subseteq (A_1 \vartriangle B_1) \cup (A_2 \vartriangle B_2),$$

it follows that

(5) $\quad \mu^*[(A_1 \cup A_2) \vartriangle (B_1 \cup B_2)] \leq \mu^*(A_1 \vartriangle B_1) + \mu^*(A_2 \vartriangle B_2) < \epsilon.$

Since $B_1 \cup B_2$ is an elementary set, it follows from Theorem 4 that $A_1 \cup A_2$ is measurable.

But in view of the definition of measurable set, if A is measurable, so is $E \setminus A$; hence, $A_1 \cap A_2$ is measurable because of the relation

$$A_1 \cap A_2 = E \setminus [(E \setminus A_1) \cup (E \setminus A_2)].$$

COROLLARY. *The difference and symmetric difference of two measurable sets are measurable.*

This follows from Theorem 6 and the relations

$$A_1 \setminus A_2 = A_1 \cap (E \setminus A_2),$$
$$A_1 \vartriangle A_2 = (A_1 \setminus A_2) \cup (A_2 \setminus A_1).$$

THEOREM 7. *If $A_1, \cdots, A_n$ are pairwise disjoint measurable sets, then*

$$\mu(\textstyle\bigcup_{k=1}^{n} A_k) = \sum_{k=1}^{n} \mu(A_k).$$

Proof. As in Theorem 6, it is sufficient to consider the case $n = 2$. Choose an arbitrary $\epsilon > 0$ and elementary sets B_1 and B_2 such that

(6) $$\mu^*(A_1 \vartriangle B_1) < \epsilon,$$

(7) $$\mu^*(A_2 \vartriangle B_2) < \epsilon.$$

Set $A = A_1 \cup A_2$ and $B = B_1 \cup B_2$. According to Theorem 6, the set A is measurable. Since

$$B_1 \cap B_2 \subseteq (A_1 \vartriangle B_1) \cup (A_2 \vartriangle B_2),$$

(8) $$m'(B_1 \cap B_2) \leq 2\epsilon.$$

In virtue of the Lemma to Theorem 5, (6) and (7) imply that

(9) $$| m'(B_1) - \mu^*(A_1) | < \epsilon,$$

(10) $$| \, m'(B_2) - \mu^*(A_2) \, | < \epsilon.$$

Since the measure is additive on the class of elementary sets, (8), (9) and (10) yield

$$m'(B) = m'(B_1) + m'(B_2) - m'(B_1 \cap B_2) \geq \mu^*(A_1) + \mu^*(A_2) - 4\epsilon.$$

Noting that $A \, \Delta \, B \subseteq (A_1 \, \Delta \, B_1) \cup (A_2 \, \Delta \, B_2)$, we finally have

$$\mu^*(A) \geq m'(B) - \mu^*(A \, \Delta \, B) \geq m'(B) - 2\epsilon \geq \mu^*(A_1) + \mu^*(A_2) - 6\epsilon.$$

Since 6ϵ may be chosen arbitrarily small,

$$\mu^*(A) \geq \mu^*(A_1) + \mu^*(A_2).$$

Inasmuch as the converse inequality

$$\mu^*(A) \leq \mu^*(A_1) + \mu^*(A_2)$$

is always true for $A = A_1 \cup A_2$, we have

$$\mu^*(A) = \mu^*(A_1) + \mu^*(A_2).$$

Since A_1, A_2 and A are measurable, μ^* can be replaced by μ, and this proves the theorem.

THEOREM 8. *The union and intersection of a countable number of measurable sets are measurable sets.*

Proof. Let

$$A_1, \cdots, A_n, \cdots$$

be a countable collection of measurable sets, and let $A = \bigcup_{n=1}^{\infty} A_n$. Set $A_n' = A_n \setminus \bigcup_{k=1}^{n-1} A_k$. It is clear that $A = \bigcup_{n=1}^{\infty} A_n'$ and that the sets A_n' are pairwise disjoint. By Theorem 6 and its Corollary, all the sets A_n' are measurable. According to Theorems 7 and 3,

$$\sum_{k=1}^{n} \mu(A_k') = \mu(\bigcup_{k=1}^{n} A_k') \leq \mu(A)$$

for arbitrary finite n. Therefore, the series

$$\sum_{n=1}^{\infty} \mu(A_n')$$

converges, and consequently for arbitrary $\epsilon > 0$ there exists an N such that

(11) $$\sum_{n>N} \mu(A_n') < \epsilon/2.$$

Since the set $C = \bigcup_{n=1}^{N} A_n'$ is measurable (as a union of a finite number of measurable sets), there exists an elementary set B such that

(12) $$\mu^*(C \, \Delta \, B) < \epsilon/2.$$

Inasmuch as

$$A \, \Delta \, B \subseteq (C \, \Delta \, B) \cup (\bigcup_{n>N} A_n'),$$

(11) and (12) imply that

$$\mu^*(A \bigtriangleup B) < \epsilon.$$

Hence, by Theorem 5, the set A is measurable.

Since the complement of a measurable set is measurable, the second half of the theorem follows from the relation

$$\bigcap_n A_n = E \setminus \bigcup_n (E \setminus A_n).$$

Theorem 8 is a generalization of Theorem 6. The following theorem is the corresponding generalization of Theorem 7.

THEOREM 9. *If $\{A_n\}$ is a sequence of pairwise disjoint measurable sets, and $A = \bigcup_n A_n$, then*

$$\mu(A) = \sum_n \mu(A_n).$$

Proof. By Theorem 7, for arbitrary N

$$\mu(\bigcup_{n=1}^N A_n) = \sum_{n=1}^N \mu(A_n) \leq \mu(A).$$

Letting $N \to \infty$, we obtain

(13) $$\mu(A) \geq \sum_{n=1}^\infty \mu(A_n).$$

On the other hand, according to Theorem 3,

(14) $$\mu(A) \leq \sum_{n=1}^\infty \mu(A_n).$$

The theorem follows from (13) and (14).

The property of the measure established in Theorem 9 is called *complete additivity* or *σ-additivity*. The following property of the measure, called *continuity*, is an immediate consequence of σ-additivity.

THEOREM 10. *If $A_1 \supseteq A_2 \supseteq \cdots$ is a monotone decreasing sequence of measurable sets, and $A = \bigcap_n A_n$, then*

$$\mu(A) = \lim_{n \to \infty} \mu(A_n).$$

It is obviously sufficient to consider the case $A = \emptyset$, since the general case reduces to this on replacing A_n by $A_n \setminus A$. Then

$$A_1 = (A_1 \setminus A_2) \cup (A_2 \setminus A_3) \cup \cdots$$

and

$$A_n = (A_n \setminus A_{n+1}) \cup (A_{n+1} \setminus A_{n+2}) \cup \cdots.$$

Consequently,

(15) $$\mu(A_1) = \sum_{k=1}^\infty \mu(A_k \setminus A_{k+1})$$

and

(16) $$\mu(A_n) = \sum_{k=n}^\infty \mu(A_k \setminus A_{k+1});$$

since the series (15) converges, its remainder (16) approaches zero as $n \to \infty$. Hence,

$$\mu(A_n) \to 0 \qquad\qquad (n \to \infty).$$

This is what we were to prove.

COROLLARY. *If $A_1 \subseteq A_2 \subseteq \cdots$ is a monotone increasing sequence of measurable sets and $A = \bigcup_n A_n$, then*

$$\mu(A) = \lim_{n \to \infty} \mu(A_n).$$

To prove this it is sufficient to replace the sets A_n by their complements and then to use Theorem 10.

We have now extended the measure defined on the elementary sets to the wider class of measurable sets. The latter class is closed with respect to the operations of countable unions and intersections, and the measure on this class is σ-additive.

We conclude this section with a few remarks.

1. The theorems we have proved characterize the class of Lebesgue measurable sets.

Since every open set contained in E can be written as a union of a countable number of open rectangles, that is, measurable sets, Theorem 8 implies that every open set is measurable. The closed sets are also measurable, since they are the complements of the open sets. In view of Theorem 8, all sets which can be obtained from the open and closed sets by taking countable unions and intersections are also measurable. It can be shown, however, that these sets do not exhaust the class of all Lebesgue measurable sets.

2. We have considered only plane sets contained in the unit square $E = \{0 \le x, y \le 1\}$. It is not hard to remove this restriction. This can be done, for instance, in the following way. Representing the whole plane as the union of the squares $E_{nm} = \{n \le x \le n + 1, m \le y \le m + 1 \ (m, n \text{ integers})\}$, we define a plane set A to be measurable if its intersection $A_{nm} = A \cap E_{nm}$ with each of these squares is measurable, and the series

$$\sum_{n,m} \mu(A_{nm})$$

converges. We then define

$$\mu(A) = \sum_{n,m} \mu(A_{nm}).$$

All the measure properties derived above carry over in an obvious fashion to this case.

3. In this section we have constructed Lebesgue measure for plane sets. Lebesgue measure on the line, in three dimensions, or, in general, in Euclidean n-space, can be constructed analogously. The measure in all these

cases is constructed in the same way: starting with a measure defined for a certain class of simple sets (rectangles in the plane; open, closed and half-open intervals on the line; etc.) we first define a measure for finite unions of such sets, and then extend it to the much wider class of Lebesgue measurable sets. The definition of measurable set is carried over verbatim to sets in a space of arbitrary (finite) dimension.

4. To introduce Lebesgue measure we started with the usual definition of area. The analogous construction in one dimension is based on the length of an interval. However, the concept of measure can be introduced in another, somewhat more general, way.

Let $F(t)$ be a nondecreasing and left continuous function defined on the real line. We set

$$m(a, b) = F(b) - F(a + 0),$$

$$m[a, b] = F(b + 0) - F(a),$$

$$m(a, b] = F(b + 0) - F(a + 0),$$

$$m[a, b) = F(b) - F(a).$$

It is easily verified that the interval function m defined in this way is nonnegative and additive. Proceeding in the same way as described above, we can construct a certain "measure" $\mu_F(A)$. The class of sets measurable relative to this measure is closed under the operations of countable unions and intersections, and μ_F is σ-additive. The class of μ_F-measurable sets will, in general, depend on the choice of the function F. However, the open and closed sets, and consequently their countable unions and intersections, will be measurable for arbitrary choice of F. The measures μ_F, where F is arbitrary (except for the conditions imposed above), are called Lebesgue-Stieltjes measures. In particular, the function $F(t) = t$ corresponds to the usual Lebesgue measure on the real line.

A measure μ_F which is equal to zero on every set whose Lebesgue measure is zero is said to be *absolutely continuous*. A measure μ_F whose set of values is countable [this will occur whenever the set of values of $F(t)$ is countable] is said to be *discrete*. A measure μ_F is called *singular* if it is zero on every set consisting of one point, and if there is a set M whose Lebesgue measure is zero and such that the μ_F measure of its complement is zero.

It can be proved that every measure μ_F is a sum of an absolutely continuous, a discrete and a singular measure.

★ *Existence of nonmeasurable sets.* We proved above that the class of Lebesgue measurable sets is very wide. The question naturally arises whether there exist nonmeasurable sets. We shall prove that there are such sets. The simplest example of a nonmeasurable set can be constructed on a circumference.

Let C be a circumference of length 1, and let α be an irrational number. Partition the points of C into classes by the following rule: Two points of C belong to the same class if, and only if, one can be carried into the other by a rotation of C through an angle $n\alpha$ (n an integer). Each class is clearly countable. We now select a point from each class. We show that the resulting set Φ is nonmeasurable. Denote by Φ_n the set obtained by rotating Φ through the angle $n\alpha$. It is easily seen that all the sets Φ_n are pairwise disjoint and that their union is C. If the set Φ were measurable, the sets Φ_n congruent to it would also be measurable. Since

$$C = \textstyle\bigcup_{n=-\infty}^{\infty} \Phi_n , \qquad \Phi_n \cap \Phi_m = \emptyset \qquad\qquad (n \neq m),$$

the σ-additivity of the measure would imply that

(17) $$\textstyle\sum_{n=-\infty}^{\infty} \mu(\Phi_n) = 1.$$

But congruent sets must have the same measure:

$$\mu(\Phi_n) = \mu(\Phi).$$

The last equality shows that (17) is impossible, since the sum of the series on the left side of (17) is zero if $\mu(\Phi) = 0$, and is infinity if $\mu(\Phi) > 0$. Hence, the set Φ (and consequently every set Φ_n) is nonmeasurable. ★

EXERCISES

1. If A is a countable set of points contained in

$$E = \{(x, y) : 0 \le x \le 1, 0 \le y \le 1\},$$

then A is measurable and $\mu(A) = 0$.

2. Let $F_0 = [0, 1]$ and let F be the Cantor set constructed on F_0 (see vol. 1, pp. 32–33). Prove that $\mu_1(F) = 0$, where $\mu_1(F)$ is the (linear) Lebesgue measure of F.

3. Let F be as in Ex. 2. If $x \in F$, then

$$x = a_1/3 + \cdots + a_n/3^n + \cdots,$$

where $a_1 = 0$ or 2. Define

$$\varphi(x) = a_1/2^2 + \cdots + a_n/2^{n+1} + \cdots \qquad\qquad (x \in F)$$

(see the reference given in Ex. 2). The function φ is single-valued. If a, $b \in F$ are such that $(a, b) \notin F$ [i.e., (a, b) is a deleted open interval in the construction of F], show that $\varphi(a) = \varphi(b)$. We can therefore define φ on $[a, b]$ as equal to this common value. The function φ so defined on $F_0 = [0, 1]$ is nondecreasing and continuous. Show that μ_φ, the Lebesgue-Stieltjes measure generated by φ on the set F_0, is a singular measure. The function φ is called the Cantor function.

4. For $E = \{(x, y) : 0 \le x \le 1, 0 \le y \le 1\}$, $A \subset E$ we can restate our definition for the measurability of A as follows: A is measurable provided

$$\mu^*(E) = \mu^*(E \cap A) + \mu^*(E \setminus A).$$

Show that A satisfies the measurability criterion of Carathéodory: For every $F \subseteq E$,

$$\mu^*(F) = \mu^*(F \cap A) + \mu^*(F \setminus A).$$

The converse implication is, of course, trivial.

5. Lebesgue measure in the plane is *regular*, i.e.,

$$\mu^*(A) = \inf \{\mu(G) : A \subseteq G, G \text{ open relative to } E\}.$$

6. Derive Lebesgue's criterion for measurability: A set $A \subseteq E$ is measurable if, and only if, for every $\epsilon > 0$ there exist G open (relative to E) and F closed such that $F \subset A \subset G$ and $\mu(G \setminus F) < \epsilon$. (See the definition of Jordan measurability in §36.) Hint: Apply Ex. 5 to A and $E \setminus A$.

§34. Collections of sets

Our discussion of the abstract theory of measure will presuppose certain facts about collections of sets, in addition to the elementary theory of sets presented in Chapter I.

A collection of sets is a set whose elements are themselves sets. As a rule, we shall consider collections of sets whose elements are subsets of a fixed set X. In general, collections of sets will be denoted by capital German letters. Fundamentally, we shall be interested in collections of sets which are closed under some (or all) of the operations introduced in Chapter I, §1.

DEFINITION 1. A *ring* is a nonempty collection of sets $\mathfrak{R}$ with the property that $A \in \mathfrak{R}$, $B \in \mathfrak{R}$ imply that $A \bigtriangleup B \in \mathfrak{R}$ and $A \cap B \in \mathfrak{R}$.

Since

$$A \cup B = (A \bigtriangleup B) \bigtriangleup (A \cap B),$$

$$A \setminus B = A \bigtriangleup (A \cap B)$$

for arbitrary A and B, it follows that $A \in \mathfrak{R}$, $B \in \mathfrak{R}$ imply that $A \cup B \in \mathfrak{R}$ and $A \setminus B \in \mathfrak{R}$. Hence a ring of sets is a collection of sets closed under unions, intersections, differences and symmetric differences (of pairs of sets). Clearly, a ring is also closed under finite unions and intersections:

$$C = \bigcup_{k=1}^{n} A_k, \qquad D = \bigcap_{k=1}^{n} A_k.$$

Every ring contains the empty set $\emptyset$, since $A \setminus A = \emptyset$. A ring consisting of the empty set alone is the smallest possible ring.

A set E is called a *unit* of a collection of sets $\mathfrak{S}$ if it is an element of $\mathfrak{S}$ and if

$$A \cap E = A$$

for arbitrary $A \in \mathfrak{S}$. It is easily seen that if $\mathfrak{S}$ has a unit, it is unique.

Hence, the unit of a collection of sets $\mathfrak{S}$ is the maximal set of the collection, that is, the set which contains every other element of $\mathfrak{S}$.

A ring of sets with a unit is called an *algebra* of sets. [TRANS. NOTE. This definition leads to difficulties in the statements and proofs of certain theorems in the sequel. These difficulties disappear if the usual definition of an algebra is used: Let X be a set, $\mathfrak{S}$ a collection of subsets of X. The collection $\mathfrak{S}$ is called an *algebra* if $\mathfrak{S}$ is a ring with unit $E = X$.]

EXAMPLES. 1. If A is an arbitrary set, the collection $\mathfrak{M}(A)$ of all its subsets is an algebra of sets with unit $E = A$.

2. If A is an arbitrary nonempty set, the collection $\{\emptyset, A\}$ consisting of the set A and the empty set $\emptyset$ is an algebra with unit $E = A$.

3. The set of all finite subsets of an arbitrary set A is a ring. This ring is an algebra if, and only if, A is finite.

4. The set of all bounded subsets of the real line is a ring without a unit.

An immediate consequence of the definition of a ring is

THEOREM 1. *The intersection* $\mathfrak{R} = \bigcap_\alpha \mathfrak{R}_\alpha$ *of an arbitrary number of rings is a ring.*

We shall prove the following simple, but important, proposition:

THEOREM 2. *If $\mathfrak{S}$ is an arbitrary nonempty collection of sets, there exists precisely one ring $\mathfrak{R}(\mathfrak{S})$ containing $\mathfrak{S}$ and contained in every ring $\mathfrak{R}$ containing $\mathfrak{S}$.*

Proof. It is easy to see that the ring $\mathfrak{R}(\mathfrak{S})$ is uniquely determined by $\mathfrak{S}$. To show that it exists, we consider the union $X = \bigcup_{A \in \mathfrak{S}} A$ and the ring $\mathfrak{M}(X)$ of all the subsets of X. Let Σ be the collection of all rings contained in $\mathfrak{M}(X)$ and containing $\mathfrak{S}$. The intersection

$$\mathfrak{P} = \bigcap_{\mathfrak{R} \in \Sigma} \mathfrak{R}$$

is obviously the required ring $\mathfrak{R}(\mathfrak{S})$.

For, if $\mathfrak{R}^*$ is a ring containing $\mathfrak{S}$, then $\mathfrak{R} = \mathfrak{R}^* \cap \mathfrak{M}(X)$ is a ring in Σ; hence,

$$\mathfrak{S} \subseteq \mathfrak{P} \subseteq \mathfrak{R} \subseteq \mathfrak{R}^*,$$

that is, $\mathfrak{P}$ is minimal. $\mathfrak{R}(\mathfrak{S})$ is called the *minimal ring over the collection* $\mathfrak{S}$. [$\mathfrak{R}(\mathfrak{S})$ is also called the *ring generated by* $\mathfrak{S}$.]

The actual construction of the ring $\mathfrak{R}(\mathfrak{S})$ over a prescribed collection $\mathfrak{S}$ is, in general, quite complicated. However, it becomes completely explicit in the important special case when $\mathfrak{S}$ is a semi-ring.

DEFINITION 2. A collection of sets $\mathfrak{S}$ is called a *semi-ring* if it satisfies the following conditions:

(1) $\mathfrak{S}$ contains the empty set $\emptyset$.

(2) If A, $B \in \mathfrak{S}$, then $A \cap B \in \mathfrak{S}$.

(3) If A and $A_1 \subseteq A$ are both elements of $\mathfrak{S}$, then

$$A = \bigcup_{k=1}^{n} A_k \, ,$$

where the sets A_k are pairwise disjoint elements of $\mathfrak{S}$, and the first of the sets A_k is the given set A_1.

In the sequel we shall call a collection of pairwise disjoint sets

$$A_1, \, \cdots, A_n \, ,$$

whose union is a set A, a *finite partition* of the set A.

Every ring $\mathfrak{R}$ is a semi-ring, since if both A and $A_1 \subseteq A$ belong to $\mathfrak{R}$, then $A = A_1 \cup A_2$, where $A_2 = A \setminus A_1 \in \mathfrak{R}$.

An example of a semi-ring which is not a ring is the collection of all open, closed and half-open intervals on the real line. [Among the intervals we include, of course, the empty interval (a, a) and the interval consisting of one point $[a, a]$.]

In order to show how the minimal ring over a semi-ring is constructed, we derive several properties of semi-rings.

LEMMA 1. *Suppose that* $A_1, \, \cdots, A_n, A$ *are all elements of a semi-ring* $\mathfrak{S}$, *where the sets* A_i *are pairwise disjoint subsets of* A. *Then there is a finite partition of* A:

$$A = \bigcup_{k=1}^{s} A_k \qquad (s \geq n, A_k \in \mathfrak{S}),$$

whose first n *terms are the sets* A_i $(1 \leq i \leq n)$.

The proof is by induction. The assertion is true for $n = 1$ by the definition of a semi-ring. We assume that the proposition is true for $n = m$ and consider $m + 1$ sets $A_1, \, \cdots, A_m, A_{m+1}$ satisfying the hypothesis of the lemma. In view of the inductive hypothesis,

$$A = A_1 \cup A_2 \cup \cdots \cup A_m \cup B_1 \cup B_2 \cup \cdots \cup B_p \, ,$$

where all the sets B_q $(1 \leq q \leq p)$ are elements of $\mathfrak{S}$. Set

$$B_{q1} = A_{m+1} \cap B_q \, .$$

By the definition of a semi-ring there is a partition

$$B_q = B_{q1} \cup B_{q2} \cup \cdots \cup B_{qr_q} \, ,$$

where all the sets B_{qj} are elements of $\mathfrak{S}$. It is easy to see that

$$A = A_1 \cup \cdots \cup A_m \cup A_{m+1} \cup \bigcup_{q=1}^{p} \bigcup_{j=2}^{r_q} B_{qj} \, .$$

Hence, the lemma is true for $n = m + 1$, and so for all n.

LEMMA 2. *If A_1, $\cdots$, A_n are elements of a semi-ring $\mathfrak{S}$, there exists in $\mathfrak{S}$ a finite set of pairwise disjoint sets B_1, $\cdots$, B_t such that each A_k can be written as a union*

$$A_k = \bigcup_{s \in M_k} B_s$$

of some of the sets B_s.

Proof. The lemma is trivial for $n = 1$, since it is then enough to put $t = 1$, $B_1 = A_1$. Suppose that the lemma is true for $n = m$ and consider a collection of sets A_1, $\cdots$, A_{m+1}. Let B_1, $\cdots$, B_t be elements of $\mathfrak{S}$ satisfying the conditions of the lemma relative to the sets A_1, $\cdots$, A_m. Set

$$B_{s1} = A_{m+1} \cap B_s.$$

By Lemma 1, there exists a partition

$$(1) \qquad A_{m+1} = \bigcup_{s=1}^{t} B_{s1} \cup \bigcup_{p=1}^{q} B_p' \qquad (B_p' \in \mathfrak{S}),$$

and in view of the definition of a semi-ring there exists a partition

$$B_s = B_{s1} \cup B_{s2} \cup \cdots \cup B_{sf_s} \qquad (B_{sq} \in \mathfrak{S}).$$

It is easily seen that

$$A_k = \bigcup_{s \in M_k} \bigcup_{q=1}^{f_s} B_{sq} \qquad (1 \le k \le m),$$

and that the sets B_{sq}, B_p' are pairwise disjoint. Hence, the sets B_{sq}, B_p' satisfy the lemma relative to the sets A_1, $\cdots$, A_m, A_{m+1}. This proves the lemma.

LEMMA 3. *If $\mathfrak{S}$ is a semi-ring, then $\mathfrak{R}(\mathfrak{S})$ coincides with the collection $\mathfrak{Z}$ of the sets A which admit of a finite partition*

$$A = \bigcup_{k=1}^{n} A_k \qquad (A_k \in \mathfrak{S}).$$

Proof. We show that $\mathfrak{Z}$ is a ring. If $A, B \in \mathfrak{Z}$, then

$$A = \bigcup_{k=1}^{n} A_k, \qquad B = \bigcup_{k=1}^{m} B_k \qquad (A_k, B_k \in \mathfrak{S}).$$

Since $\mathfrak{S}$ is a semi-ring, the sets

$$C_{ij} = A_i \cap B_j$$

are also elements of $\mathfrak{S}$. By Lemma 1,

$$(2) \qquad A_i = \bigcup_j C_{ij} \cup \bigcup_{k=1}^{r_i} D_{ik}; \qquad B_j = \bigcup_i C_{ij} \cup \bigcup_{k=1}^{s_i} E_{jk},$$

where D_{ik}, $E_{jk} \in \mathfrak{S}$. The equality (2) implies that

$$A \cap B = \bigcup_{i,j} C_{ij},$$

$$A \triangle B = \bigcup_{i,k} D_{ik} \cup \bigcup_{j,k} E_{jk}.$$

Therefore, $A \cap B$ and $A \triangle B$ are elements of $\mathcal{Z}$. Hence $\mathcal{Z}$ is a ring, and it is obvious that it is the minimal ring containing $\mathfrak{S}$.

In various problems, especially in measure theory, it is necessary to consider denumerable, as well as finite, unions and intersections. It is therefore necessary to introduce, in addition to the definition of a ring, the following definitions.

DEFINITION 3. A ring $\mathfrak{R}$ of sets is called a *σ-ring* if $A_i \in \mathfrak{R}$ $(i = 1, 2, \cdots)$ implies that

$$S = \mathsf{U}_n \, A_n \in \mathfrak{R}.$$

DEFINITION 4. A ring of sets $\mathfrak{R}$ is called a *δ-ring* if $A_i \in \mathfrak{R}$ $(i = 1, 2, \cdots)$ implies that

$$D = \mathsf{\cap}_n \, A_n \in \mathfrak{R}.$$

It is natural to call a σ-ring (δ-ring) with a unit a σ-algebra (δ-algebra). However, it is easy to see that these two notions coincide: every σ-algebra is a δ-algebra and every δ-algebra is a σ-algebra. This follows from de Morgan's laws:

$$\mathsf{U}_n \, A_n = E \setminus \mathsf{\cap}_n \, (E \setminus A_n),$$
$$\mathsf{\cap}_n \, A_n = E \setminus \mathsf{U}_n \, (E \setminus A_n)$$

(see Chapter 1, §1). σ-algebras, or δ-algebras, are called *Borel algebras*; or, briefly, *B-algebras*.

The simplest example of a B-algebra is the collection of all subsets of a set A.

For B-algebras there is a theorem analogous to Theorem 2, which was proved above for rings.

THEOREM 4. *If $\mathfrak{S}$ is a nonempty collection of sets, there exists a B-algebra $\mathfrak{B}(\mathfrak{S})$ containing $\mathfrak{S}$ and contained in every B-algebra containing $\mathfrak{S}$.*

The proof (see Trans. Note, p. 16) is carried out in exactly the same way as the proof of Theorem 2. The B-algebra $\mathfrak{B}(\mathfrak{S})$ is called the *minimal B-algebra over the system* $\mathfrak{S}$ or the *Borel closure of* $\mathfrak{S}$.

In analysis an important part is played by the *Borel sets* or *B-sets*, which may be defined as the elements of the minimal B-algebra over the set of all closed intervals $[a, b]$ on the real line (or the set of all open intervals, or the set of half-closed intervals).

To supplement §7 of Chapter 1 we note the following facts, which will be required in Chapter VI.

Let $y = f(x)$ be a function defined on a set M with values in a set N. Denote by $f(\mathfrak{M})$ the collection of all images $f(A)$ of sets in $\mathfrak{M}$, where $\mathfrak{M}$ is a set of subsets of M. Similarly, let $f^{-1}(\mathfrak{N})$ be the collection of all inverse images $f^{-1}(A)$, where $\mathfrak{N}$ is a set of subsets of N. Then:

1. If $\mathfrak{R}$ is a ring, $f^{-1}(\mathfrak{R})$ is a ring.
2. If $\mathfrak{R}$ is an algebra, $f^{-1}(\mathfrak{R})$ is an algebra.
3. If $\mathfrak{R}$ is a B-algebra, $f^{-1}(\mathfrak{R})$ is a B-algebra.
4. $\mathfrak{R}(f^{-1}(\mathfrak{R})) = f^{-1}(\mathfrak{R}(\mathfrak{R}))$.
5. $\mathfrak{B}(f^{-1}(\mathfrak{R})) = f^{-1}(\mathfrak{B}(\mathfrak{R}))$.

★ Let $\mathfrak{R}$ be a ring of sets. If the operations $A \,\Delta\, B$ and $A \cap B$ are regarded as addition and multiplication, respectively, then $\mathfrak{R}$ is a ring in the usual algebraic sense. All its elements satisfy the conditions

$$(*) \qquad\qquad a + a = 0, \qquad a^2 = a.$$

A ring all of whose elements satisfy the conditions $(*)$ is called a Boolean ring. Every Boolean ring can be realized as a ring of sets with the operations $A \,\Delta\, B$ and $A \cap B$ (Stone). ★

EXERCISES

1. Suppose that $\mathfrak{R}$ is a ring of subsets of a set X and that $\mathfrak{A}$ is the collection of those sets $E \subseteq X$ for which either $E \in \mathfrak{R}$ or else $X \setminus E \in \mathfrak{R}$. Show that $\mathfrak{A}$ is an algebra with unit X.

2. Determine the minimal ring $\mathfrak{R}(\mathfrak{S})$ in each of the following cases:
(a) for a fixed subset $A \subseteq X$, $\mathfrak{S} = \{A\}$;
(b) for a fixed subset $A \subseteq X$, $\mathfrak{S} = \{B : A \subseteq B \subseteq X\}$.

3. Let $\mathfrak{S}$ be a semi-ring in X, and let $\mathfrak{R}(\mathfrak{S})$ be the minimal ring over $\mathfrak{S}$. Then the minimal σ-rings over $\mathfrak{S}$ and $\mathfrak{R}(\mathfrak{S})$ coincide.

4. For each of the following sets what are the σ-ring and the Borel algebra generated by the given class of sets $\mathfrak{S}$?
(a) Let T be a one-to-one onto transformation of X with itself. A subset $A \subseteq X$ is called invariant if $x \in A$ implies that $T(x) \in A$ and $T^{-1}(x) \in A$. Let $\mathfrak{S}$ be the collection of invariant subsets of X.
(b) Let X be the plane and let $\mathfrak{S}$ be the collection of all subsets of the plane which can be covered by countably many horizontal lines.

§35. Measures on semi-rings. Extension of a measure on a semi-ring to the minimal ring over the semi-ring

In §33, to define a measure in the plane we started with the measure (area) of rectangles and then extended this measure to a more general class of sets. The results and methods of §33 are completely general and can be extended, with no essential changes, to measures defined on arbitrary sets. The first step in the construction of a measure in the plane is the extension of the measure of rectangles to elementary sets, that is, to finite unions of pairwise disjoint rectangles.

We consider the abstract analogue of this problem in this section.

DEFINITION 1. A set function $\mu(A)$ is called a *measure* if

1) its domain of definition S_μ is a semi-ring;
2) its values are real and nonnegative;
3) it is additive, that is, if

$$A = \bigcup_k A_k$$

is a finite partition of a set $A \in S_\mu$ in sets $A_k \in S_\mu$, then

$$\mu(A) = \sum_k \mu(A_k).$$

REMARK. Since $\emptyset = \emptyset \cup \emptyset$, it follows that $\mu(\emptyset) = 2\mu(\emptyset)$, i.e., $\mu(\emptyset) = 0\cdot$
The following two theorems on measures in semi-rings will be applied repeatedly in the sequel.

THEOREM 1. *Let μ be a measure defined on a semi-ring S_μ. If*

$$A_1, \cdots, A_n, A \in S_\mu,$$

where the sets A_k are pairwise disjoint subsets of A, then

$$\sum_{k=1}^n \mu(A_k) \leq \mu(A).$$

Proof. Since S_μ is a semi-ring, in view of Lemma 1 of §34 there exists a partition

$$A = \bigcup_{k=1}^s A_k \qquad\qquad (s \geq n,\ A_k \in S_\mu)$$

in which the first n sets coincide with the given sets $A_1, \cdots, A_n$. Since the measure of an arbitrary set is nonnegative,

$$\sum_{k=1}^n \mu(A_k) \leq \sum_{k=1}^s \mu(A_k) = \mu(A).$$

THEOREM 2. *If $A_1, \cdots, A_n, A \in S_\mu$ and $A \subseteq \bigcup_{k=1}^n A_k$, then*

$$\mu(A) \leq \sum_{k=1}^n \mu(A_k).$$

Proof. According to Lemma 2 of §34 there exist pairwise disjoint set[s] $B_1, \cdots, B_t \in S_\mu$ such that each of the sets $A, A_1, \cdots, A_n$ can be written as a union of some of the sets B_s:

$$A = \bigcup_{s \in M_0} B_s ; \qquad A_k = \bigcup_{s \in M_k} B_s \qquad (1 \leq k \leq n)$$

where each index $s \in M_0$ is an element of some M_k. Consequently, every term of the sum

$$\sum_{s \in M_0} \mu(B_s) = \mu(A)$$

appears at least once in the double sum

$$\sum_{k=1}^n \sum_{s \in M_k} \mu(B_s) = \sum_{k=1}^n \mu(A_k).$$

Hence,

$$\mu(A) \leq \sum_{k=1}^n \mu(A_k).$$

In particular, if $n = 1$, we obtain the

COROLLARY. *If $A \subseteq A'$, then $\mu(A) \leq \mu(A')$.*

DEFINITION 2. A measure $\mu(A)$ is said to be an *extension of a measure* $m(A)$ if $S_m \subseteq S_\mu$ and if $\mu(A) = m(A)$ for every $A \in S_m$.

The primary purpose of this section is to prove the following theorem.

THEOREM 3. *Every measure $m(A)$ has a unique extension $\mu(A)$ whose domain of definition is the ring $\mathfrak{R}(S_m)$.*

Proof. For each set $A \in \mathfrak{R}(S_m)$ there exists a partition

$$(1) \qquad\qquad A = \bigcup_{k=1}^n B_k \qquad\qquad (B_k \in S_m)$$

(§34, Theorem 3). We set, by definition,

$$(2) \qquad\qquad \mu(A) = \sum_{k=1}^n m(B_k).$$

It is easily seen that the value of $\mu(A)$ defined by (2) is independent of the choice of the partition (1). In fact, let

$$A = \bigcup_{i=1}^m B_i = \bigcup_{j=1}^n C_j \qquad (B_i \in S_m, C_j \in S_m)$$

be two partitions of A. Since all the intersections $B_i \cap C_j$ belong to S_m, in view of the additivity of the measure m,

$$\sum_i m(B_i) = \sum_{i=1}^m \sum_{j=1}^n m(B_i \cap C_j) = \sum_j m(C_j).$$

The measure $\mu(A)$ defined by (2) is obviously nonnegative and additive. This proves the existence of an extension $\mu(A)$ of the measure m. To prove its uniqueness, we note that, according to the definition of an extension, if $A = \bigcup_{k=1}^n B_k$, where the B_k are disjoint elements of S_m, then

$$\mu^*(A) = \sum \mu^*(B_k) = \sum m(B_k) = \mu(A)$$

for an arbitrary extension μ^* of m over $\mathfrak{R}(S_m)$. This proves the theorem.

The relation of this theorem to the constructions of §33 will be fully clear if we note that the set of all rectangles in the plane is a semi-ring, that the area of the rectangles is a measure in the sense of Def. 1 and that the class of elementary plane sets is the minimal ring over the semi-ring of rectangles.

EXERCISES

1. Let X be the set of positive integers, $\mathfrak{S}$ the set of all finite subsets of X. Suppose that $\sum_{n=1}^\infty u_n$ is a convergent series of positive numbers. For $A \in \mathfrak{S}$ define $\mu(A) = \sum u_n$ $(n \in A)$. Prove that μ is a measure. Now suppose that $\mathfrak{P}$ is the set of all subsets of X and that μ is defined as above for finite subsets of X, but that $\mu(A) = +\infty$ if A is infinite. μ is still finitely additive [although $\mu(A)$ may equal $+\infty$ for some sets]. However, μ is not completely additive (see §37, Def. 1).

2 Let X be the plane, and let $\mathfrak{S} = \{A : A =$ the set of all (x, y) such that $a < x \leq b, y = c\}$, i.e., $\mathfrak{S}$ consists of all the horizontal right half-closed line segments. Define $\mu(A) = b - a$.

(a) Show that $\mathfrak{S}$ is a semi-ring.

(b) Show that μ is a measure on $\mathfrak{S}$.

3. Let μ be a measure on a ring $\mathfrak{R}$.

(a) For $A, B \in \mathfrak{R}$ show that $\mu(A \cup B) = \mu(A) + \mu(B) - \mu(A \cap B)$.

(b) For $A, B, C \in \mathfrak{R}$ show that

$$\mu(A \cup B \cup C) = \mu(A) + \mu(B) + \mu(C)$$
$$- [\mu(A \cap B) + \mu(B \cap C) + \mu(C \cap A)] + \mu(A \cap B \cap C).$$

(c) Generalize to the case $A_1, \cdots, A_n \in \mathfrak{R}$.

§36. Extension of the Jordan measure

The concept of Jordan measure is of historical and practical interest, but will not be used in the sequel.

In this section we shall consider the general form of the process which in the case of plane figures is used to pass from the definition of the areas of finite unions of rectangles with sides parallel to the coordinate axes to the areas of those figures which are assigned definite areas in elementary geometry or classical analysis. This transition was described with complete clarity by the French mathematician Jordan about 1880. Jordan's basic idea, however, goes back to the mathematicians of ancient Greece and consists in approximating the "measurable" sets A by sets A' and A'' such that

$$A' \subseteq A \subseteq A''.$$

Since an arbitrary measure can be extended to a ring (§35, Theorem 3), it is natural to assume that the initial measure m is defined on the ring $\mathfrak{R} = \mathfrak{R}(S_m)$. We shall make this assumption in the rest of this section.

DEFINITION 1. We shall say that a set A is *Jordan measurable* if for every $\epsilon > 0$ there are sets $A', A'' \in \mathfrak{R}$ such that

$$A' \subseteq A \subseteq A'', \qquad m(A'' \setminus A') < \epsilon.$$

THEOREM 1. *The collection $\mathfrak{R}^*$ of sets which are Jordan measurable is a ring.*

For, suppose that $A, B \in \mathfrak{R}^*$; then for arbitrary $\epsilon > 0$ there exist sets $A', A'', B', B'' \in \mathfrak{R}$ such that

$$A' \subseteq A \subseteq A'', \qquad B' \subseteq B \subseteq B''$$

and

$$m(A'' \setminus A') < \epsilon/2, \qquad m(B'' \setminus B') < \epsilon/2.$$

Hence

(1) $$A' \cup B' \subseteq A \cup B \subseteq A'' \cup B'',$$

(2) $$A' \setminus B'' \subseteq A \setminus B \subseteq A'' \setminus B'.$$

Since

$$(A'' \cup B'') \setminus (A' \cup B') \subseteq (A'' \setminus A') \cup (B'' \setminus B'),$$

(3)
$$\begin{aligned}
m[(A'' \cup B'') \setminus (A' \cup B')] &\leq m[(A'' \setminus A') \cup (B'' \setminus B')] \\
&\leq m(A'' \setminus A') + m(B'' \setminus B') \\
&< \epsilon/2 + \epsilon/2 = \epsilon.
\end{aligned}$$

Since

$$(A'' \setminus B') \setminus (A' \setminus B'') \subseteq (A'' \setminus A') \cup (B'' \setminus B'),$$

(4)
$$\begin{aligned}
m[(A'' \setminus B') \setminus (A' \setminus B'')] &\leq m(A'' \setminus A') \cup (B'' \setminus B')] \\
&\leq m(A'' \setminus A') + m(B'' \setminus B') \\
&< \epsilon/2 + \epsilon/2 = \epsilon.
\end{aligned}$$

Inasmuch as $\epsilon > 0$ is arbitrary and the sets $A' \cup B'$, $A'' \cup B''$, $A' \setminus B''$, $A'' \setminus B'$ are elements of $\Re$, (1), (2), (3) and (4) imply that $A \cup B$ and $A \setminus B$ are elements of $\Re^*$.

Let $\mathfrak{M}$ be the collection consisting of the sets A for which there is a set $B \in \Re$ such that $B \supseteq A$. For arbitrary $A \in \mathfrak{M}$ we define

$$\bar{\mu}(A) = \inf \{m(B); B \supseteq A\},$$

$$\underline{\mu}(A) = \sup \{m(B); B \subseteq A\}.$$

The functions $\bar{\mu}(A)$ and $\underline{\mu}(A)$ are called the *outer* and *inner* measures, respectively, of the set A.

Obviously,

$$\underline{\mu}(A) \leq \bar{\mu}(A).$$

THEOREM 2. *The ring $\Re^*$ coincides with the system of all sets $A \in \mathfrak{M}$ such that $\underline{\mu}(A) = \bar{\mu}(A)$.*

Proof. If

$$\bar{\mu}(A) \neq \underline{\mu}(A),$$

then

$$\bar{\mu}(A) - \mu(A) = h > 0,$$

and

$$m(A') \le \mu(A), \qquad m(A'') \ge \bar{\mu}(A),$$

$$m(A'' \setminus A') = m(A'') - m(A') \ge h > 0$$

for arbitrary A', $A'' \in \Re$ such that $A' \subseteq A \subseteq A''$. Hence $A \notin \Re^*$.
Conversely, if

$$\mu(A) = \bar{\mu}(A),$$

then for arbitrary $\epsilon > 0$ there exist A', $A'' \in \Re$ such that

$$A' \subseteq A \subseteq A'',$$

$$\mu(A) - m(A') < \epsilon/2,$$

$$m(A'') - \bar{\mu}(A) < \epsilon/2,$$

$$m(A'' \setminus A') = m(A'') - m(A') < \epsilon,$$

i.e., $A \in \Re^*$.

The following theorem holds for sets of $\mathfrak{M}$.

THEOREM 3. *If* $A \subseteq \bigcup_{k=1}^{n} A_k$, *then* $\bar{\mu}(A) \le \sum_{k=1}^{n} \bar{\mu}(A_k)$.

Proof. Choose an A_k' such that

$$A_k \subseteq A_k', \qquad m(A_k') \le \bar{\mu}(A_k) + \epsilon/2^k,$$

and let $A' = \bigcup_{k=1}^{n} A_k'$. Then

$$m(A') \le \sum_{k=1}^{n} m(A_k') \le \sum_{k=1}^{n} \bar{\mu}(A_k) + \epsilon,$$

$$\bar{\mu}(A) \le \sum_{k=1}^{n} \bar{\mu}(A_k) + \epsilon;$$

since ϵ is arbitrary, $\bar{\mu}(A) \le \sum_{k=1}^{n} \bar{\mu}(A_k)$.

THEOREM 4. *If* $A_k \subseteq A$ $(1 \le k \le n)$ *and* $A_i \cap A_j = \emptyset$, *then*

$$\mu(A) \ge \sum_{k=1}^{n} \mu(A_k).$$

Proof. Choose $A_k' \subseteq A_k$ such that $m(A_k') \ge \mu(A_k) - \epsilon/2^k$ and let $A' = \bigcup_{k=1}^{n} A_k'$. Then $A_i' \cap A_j' = \emptyset$ and

$$m(A') = \sum_{k=1}^{n} m(A_k') \ge \sum_k \mu(A_k) - \epsilon.$$

Since $A' \subseteq A$, $\mu(A) \ge m(A') \ge \sum_{k=1}^{n} \mu(A_k) - \epsilon$. Since $\epsilon > 0$ is arbitrary, $\mu(A) \ge \sum_{k=1}^{n} \mu(A_k)$.

We now define the function μ with domain of definition

$$S_\mu = \Re^*$$

as the common value of the inner and outer measures:

$$\mu(A) = \underline{\mu}(A) = \bar{\mu}(A).$$

Theorems 3 and 4 and the obvious fact that

$$\bar{\mu}(A) = \underline{\mu}(A) = m(A) \qquad\qquad (A \in \mathfrak{R})$$

imply

THEOREM 5. *The function* $\mu(A)$ *is a measure and is an extension of the measure* m.

The construction we have discussed above is applicable to an arbitrary measure m defined on a ring.

The collection $S_{m_2} = \mathfrak{S}$ of elementary sets in the plane is essentially connected with the coordinate system: the sets of the collection $\mathfrak{S}$ consist of the rectangles whose sides are parallel to the coordinate axes. In the transition to the Jordan measure

$$J^{(2)} = j(m_2)$$

this dependence on the choice of the coordinate system vanishes: if $\{\bar{x}_1, \bar{x}_2\}$ is a system of coordinates related to the original coordinate system $\{x_1, x_2\}$ by the orthogonal transformation

$$\bar{x}_1 = x_1 \cos \alpha + x_2 \sin \alpha + a_1,$$

$$\bar{x}_2 = -x_1 \sin \alpha + x_2 \cos \alpha + a_2,$$

we obtain the same Jordan measure

$$J^{(2)} = j(m_2) = j(\bar{m}_2),$$

where $\bar{m}_2$ denotes the measure constructed by means of rectangles with sides parallel to the axes $\bar{x}_1, \bar{x}_2$. This fact is justified by the following general theorem:

THEOREM 6. *In order that two Jordan extensions* $\mu_1 = j(m_1)$ *and* $\mu_2 = j(m_2)$ *of measures* m_1 *and* m_2 *defined on rings* $\mathfrak{R}_1$ *and* $\mathfrak{R}_2$ *coincide, it is necessary and sufficient that*

$$\mathfrak{R}_1 \subseteq S_{\mu_2}, \qquad m_1(A) = \mu_2(A) \quad \text{on } \mathfrak{R}_1,$$

$$\mathfrak{R}_2 \subseteq S_{\mu_1}, \qquad m_2(A) = \mu_1(A) \quad \text{on } \mathfrak{R}_2.$$

The necessity is obvious. We shall prove the sufficiency.

Suppose that $A \in S_{\mu_1}$. Then there exist $A', A'' \in \mathfrak{R}_1$ such that

$$A' \subseteq A \subseteq A'', \qquad m_1(A'') - m_1(A') < \epsilon/3,$$

and $m_1(A') \leq \mu_1(A) \leq m_1(A'')$. By hypothesis, $\mu_2(A') = m_1(A')$ and $\mu_2(A'') = m_1(A'')$.

In view of the definition of the measure μ_2 there exist sets $B', B'' \in \Re_2$ such that

$$A' \supseteq B', \quad \mu_2(A') - m_2(B') < \epsilon/3;$$
$$B'' \supseteq A'', \quad m_2(B'') - \mu_2(A'') < \epsilon/3.$$

Hence

$$B' \subseteq A \subseteq B'',$$

and, obviously,

$$m_2(B'') - m_2(B') < \epsilon.$$

Since $\epsilon > 0$ is arbitrary, $A \in S_{\mu_2}$; and the relations

$$\mu_1(B') = m_2(B') \leq \mu_2(A) \leq m_2(B'') = \mu_1(B'')$$

imply that μ_2 is an extension of μ_1. Similarly, one shows that μ_1 is an extension of μ_2, and therefore

$$\mu_2(A) = \mu_1(A).$$

This proves the theorem.

Now, to show the independence of the Jordan measure in the plane of the choice of the coordinate system we need merely show that the set obtained from an elementary set by a rotation through an angle α is Jordan measurable. It is left to the reader to carry out this proof.

If the original measure m is defined on a semi-ring instead of a ring, it is natural to call the measure

$$j(m) = j(r(m))$$

obtained by extending m over the ring $\Re(S_m)$ and then extending the latter to a Jordan measure, the Jordan extension of m.

EXERCISES

1. If AB is a line segment in the plane, then $J^{(2)}(AB) = 0$.

2. Let ABC be a right triangle in the plane, with AB perpendicular to BC and with AB and BC parallel to the x- and y-axes, respectively.

a) Show that ABC is $J^{(2)}$-measurable.

b) Using the invariance of $J^{(2)}$ under translation and reflection in an axis, show that $J^{(2)}(ABC) = \frac{1}{2}(AB)(BC)$.

3. a) It follows from Ex. 2 and the text that any triangle is $J^{(2)}$-measurable and that its $J^{(2)}$-measure is the classical area.

b) Show, therefore, that a regular polygon is $J^{(2)}$-measurable and receives its classical area.

c) It follows now that a circle, i.e., a closed disk, is $J^{(2)}$-measurable.

4. Show that the plane set $A = \{(x, y): x^2 + y^2 \leq 1, x, y \text{ rational}\}$ is not $J^{(2)}$-measurable.

§37. Complete additivity. The general problem of the extension of measures

It is often necessary to consider countable unions as well as finite unions. Therefore, the condition of additivity we imposed on a measure (§34, Def. 1) is insufficient, and it is natural to replace it by the stronger condition of complete additivity.

DEFINITION 1. A measure μ is said to be *completely additive* (or *σ-additive*) if A, A_1, $\cdots$, A_n, $\cdots$ $\in S_\mu$, where S_μ is the collection of sets on which μ is defined, and

$$A = \bigcup_{n=1}^{\infty} A_n, \qquad A_i \cap A_j = \emptyset \qquad\qquad (i \neq j)$$

imply that

$$\mu(A) = \sum_{n=1}^{\infty} \mu(A_n).$$

The plane Lebesgue measure constructed in §33 is σ-additive (Theorem 9). An altogether different example of a σ-additive measure may be constructed in the following way. Let

$$X = \{x_1, x_2, \cdots\}$$

be an arbitrary countable set and let the numbers $p_n > 0$ be such that

$$\sum_{n=1}^{\infty} p_n = 1.$$

The set S_μ consists of all the subsets of X. For each $A \subseteq X$ set

$$\mu(A) = \sum_{x_n \in A} p_n .$$

It is easy to verify that $\mu(A)$ is a σ-additive measure and that $\mu(X) = 1$. This example appears naturally in many problems in the theory of probability.

We shall also give an example of a measure which is additive, but not σ-additive. Let X be the set of all rational points on the closed interval $[0, 1]$ and let S_μ consist of the intersections of X with arbitrary intervals (a, b), $[a, b]$, $[a, b)$ or $(a, b]$. It is easily seen that S_μ is a semi-ring. For each set $A_{ab} \in S_\mu$ set

$$\mu(A_{ab}) = b - a.$$

Then μ is an additive measure. It is not σ-additive since, for instance, $\mu(X) = 1$, but X is the union of a countable number of points each of which has measure zero.

In this and the succeeding two sections we shall consider σ-additive measures and their σ-additive extensions.

THEOREM 1. *If a measure m defined on a semi-ring S_m is completely additive, then its extension $\mu = r(m)$ to the ring $\Re(S_m)$ is completely additive.*

Proof. Suppose that

$$A \in \Re(S_m), \qquad B_n \in \Re(S_m) \qquad (n = 1, 2, \cdots)$$

and that

$$A = \bigcup_{n=1}^{\infty} B_n,$$

where $B_s \cap B_r = \emptyset$ $(s \neq r)$. Then there exist sets A_j, $B_{ni} \in S_m$ such that

$$A = \bigcup_j A_j, \qquad B_n = \bigcup_i B_{ni},$$

where the sets on the right-hand sides of these equalities are pairwise disjoint and the unions are finite unions (§34, Theorem 3).

Let $C_{nij} = B_{ni} \cap A_j$. It is easy to see that the sets C_{nij} are pairwise disjoint and that

$$A_j = \bigcup_n \bigcup_i C_{nij},$$
$$B_{ni} = \bigcup_j C_{nij}.$$

Therefore, because of the complete additivity of m on S_m,

(1) $$m(A_j) = \sum_n \sum_i m(C_{nij}),$$

(2) $$m(B_{ni}) = \sum_j m(C_{nij});$$

and because of the definition of $r(m)$ on $\Re(S_m)$,

(3) $$\mu(A) = \sum_j m(A_j),$$

(4) $$\mu(B_n) = \sum_i m(B_{ni}).$$

Relations (1), (2), (3) and (4) imply that $\mu(A) = \sum_n \mu(B_n)$. (The sums over i and j are finite sums, and the series over n converge.)

It could be proved that the Jordan extension of a σ-additive measure is σ-additive, but it is not necessary to do so because it will follow from the theory of Lebesgue extensions discussed in the next section.

THEOREM 2. *If a measure μ is σ-additive and $A, A_1, \cdots, A_n, \cdots \in S_\mu$, then*

$$A \subseteq \bigcup_{n=1}^{\infty} A_n$$

implies that

$$\mu(A) \leq \sum_{n=1}^{\infty} \mu(A_n).$$

Proof. Because of Theorem 1 it is sufficient to carry out the proof for a measure defined on a ring, since the validity of Theorem 2 for $\mu = r(m)$ immediately implies its applicability to the measure m. If S_μ is a ring, the sets

$$B_n = (A \cap A_n) \setminus \bigcup_{k=1}^{n-1} A_k$$

are elements of S_μ. Since

$$A = \bigcup_{n=1}^{\infty} B_n, \qquad B_n \subseteq A_n,$$

and the sets B_n are pairwise disjoint,

$$\mu(A) = \sum_{n=1}^{\infty} \mu(B_n) \leq \sum_{n=1}^{\infty} \mu(A_n).$$

In the sequel, we shall consider only σ-additive measures, without mentioning this fact explicitly.

★ We have considered two ways of extending measures. In extending a measure m over the ring $\Re(S_m)$ in §35 we noted the uniqueness of the extension. The same is true for the Jordan extension $j(m)$ of an arbitrary measure m. If a set A is Jordan measurable with respect to a measure m (that is, $A \in S_{j(m)}$), then $\mu(A) = J(A)$, where μ is an arbitrary extension of m defined on A and $J = j(m)$ is the Jordan extension of m. It can be proved that an extension of m to a collection larger than $S_{j(m)}$ is not unique. More precisely, the following is true. Call a set A a *set of unicity* for a measure m if

1) there exists an extension of m defined on A;
2) for two such extensions μ_1 and μ_2,

$$\mu_1(A) = \mu_2(A).$$

Then the following theorem holds.

The set of sets of unicity of a measure m coincides with the collection of Jordan measurable sets relative to m, i.e., the collection of sets $S_{j(m)}$.

However, if we consider only σ-additive measures and their (σ-additive) extensions, then the collection of sets of unicity will, in general, be larger.

Since we shall be exclusively occupied with σ-additive measures in the sequel, we introduce

DEFINITION 2. A set A is said to be a *set of σ-unicity* for a σ-additive measure μ if

1) there exists a σ-additive extension λ of μ defined on A (that is, $A \in S_\lambda$);
2) if λ_1, λ_2 are two such σ-additive extensions, then

$$\lambda_1(A) = \lambda_2(A).$$

If A is a set of σ-unicity for a σ-additive measure μ, then the definition implies that if there is a σ-additive extension $\lambda(A)$ of μ defined on A, it is unique. ★

EXERCISES

1. Suppose μ is a completely additive measure on the collection of all subsets of a countable set X. Show that $\mu(A) = 0$ for all $A \subseteq X$ if, and

only if, $\mu(\{x\}) = 0$ for all $x \in X$, i.e., μ vanishes on every set consisting of a single point.

2. If X is a countable set, $\mathfrak{S}$ the class of all subsets of X and μ a completely additive measure defined on $\mathfrak{S}$, then μ must necessarily have the form of the second example after Def. 1 in §37, where, however, the p_n need only satisfy the conditions $p_n \geq 0$, $\sum p_n < \infty$.

3. Show that the measure defined in Ex. 2, §35 is completely additive. Hint: Imitate the procedure used in §33, Theorem 2.

4. Let $\mathfrak{S}$ be the semi-ring of left-closed right-open intervals on the line: $\mathfrak{S} = \{[a, b)\}$, let $F(t)$ be a nondecreasing left continuous real-valued function defined on the line and let μ_F be the Lebesgue measure defined in Remark 4 at the end of §33. Show that μ_F is completely additive by following a procedure analogous to that of Ex. 3 above. It will be necessary to show the following: Suppose that $a < b$. For $\epsilon > 0$ there exist c and d such that

$$a \leq c < d < b, \qquad [c, d] \subset [a, b)$$

and

$$\mu_F([c, d)) = F(d) - F(c) > F(b) - F(a) - \epsilon = \mu_F([a, b)) - \epsilon.$$

Similarly, there exist e, f such that $e < a < b \leq f$, $[a, b) \subset (e, f)$ and

$$\mu_F([e, f)) = F(f) - F(e) < F(b) - F(a) + \epsilon = \mu_F([a, b)) + \epsilon.$$

§38. The Lebesgue extension of a measure defined on a semi-ring with unity

Although the Jordan extension applies to a wide class of sets, it is nevertheless inadequate in many cases. Thus, for instance, if we take as the initial measure the area defined on the semi-ring of rectangles and consider the Jordan extension of this measure, then so comparatively simple a set as the set of points whose coordinates are rational and satisfy the condition $x^2 + y^2 \leq 1$ is not Jordan measurable.

The extension of a σ-additive measure defined on a semi-ring to a class of sets, which is maximal in a certain sense, can be effected by means of the Lebesgue extension. In this section we consider the Lebesgue extension of a measure defined on a semi-ring with a unit. The general case will be considered in §39.

The construction given below is to a considerable extent a repetition in abstract terms of the construction of the Lebesgue measure for plane sets in §33.

Let m be a σ-additive measure defined on a semi-ring S_m with a unit E. We define on the system $\mathfrak{S}$ of all subsets of E the functions $\mu^*(A)$ and $\mu_*(A)$ as follows.

DEFINITION 1. The *outer measure* of a set $A \subseteq E$ is

$$\mu^*(A) = \inf \{ \sum_n m(B_n) ; A \subseteq \bigcup_n B_n \},$$

where the lower bound is extended over all coverings of A by countable (finite or denumerable) collections of sets $B_n \in S_m$.

DEFINITION 2. The *inner measure* of a set $A \subseteq E$ is

$$\mu_*(A) = m(E) - \mu^*(E \setminus A).$$

Theorem 2 of §35 implies that $\mu_*(A) \leq \mu^*(A)$.

DEFINITION 3. A set $A \subseteq E$ is said to be (*Lebesgue*) *measurable* if

$$\mu_*(A) = \mu^*(A).$$

If A is measurable, the common value of $\mu_*(A) = \mu^*(A)$ is denoted by $\mu(A)$ and called the (*Lebesgue*) *measure* of A.

Obviously, if A is measurable, its complement $E \setminus A$ is also measurable. Theorem 2 of §37 immediately implies that

$$\mu_*(A) \leq \mu(A) \leq \mu^*(A)$$

for an arbitrary σ-additive extension μ of m. Therefore, for a Lebesgue measurable set A every σ-additive extension μ of m (if it exists) is equal to the common value of $\mu_*(A) = \mu^*(A)$. The Lebesgue measure is thus the σ-additive extension of m to the collection of all sets measurable in the sense of Def. 3. The definition of measurable set can obviously also be formulated as follows:

DEFINITION 3′. A set $A \subseteq E$ is said to be measurable if

$$\mu^*(A) + \mu^*(E \setminus A) = m(E).$$

It is expedient to use together with the initial measure m its extension $m' = r(m)$ (see §35) over the ring $\Re(S_m)$. It is clear that Def. 1 is equivalent to

DEFINITION 1′. The outer measure of a set A is

$$\mu^*(A) = \inf \{ \sum_n m'(B_n') ; A \in \bigcup_n B_n' \} \qquad [B_n' \in \Re(S_m)].$$

In fact, since m' is σ-additive (§37, Theorem 1), an arbitrary sum $\sum_n m'(B_n')$, where $B_n' \in \Re(S_m)$, can be replaced by an equivalent sum

$$\sum_{n,k} m(B_{nk}) \qquad\qquad (B_{nk} \in S_m),$$

where

$$B_n' = \bigcup_k B_{nk}, \qquad B_{ni} \cap B_{nj} = \emptyset \qquad\qquad (i \neq j).$$

The following is fundamental for the sequel.

THEOREM 1. *If*

$$A \subseteq \bigcup_n A_n,$$

where $\{A_n\}$ is a countable collection of sets then,

$$\mu^*(A) \leq \sum_n \mu^*(A_n).$$

THEOREM 2. *If $A \in \Re$, then $\mu_*(A) = m'(A) = \mu^*(A)$, i.e., all the sets of $\Re(S_m)$ are measurable and their outer and inner measures coincide with m'.*

THEOREM 3. *A set A is measurable if, and only if, for arbitrary $\epsilon > 0$ there exists a set $B \in \Re(S_m)$ such that*

$$\mu^*(A \triangle B) < \epsilon.$$

These propositions were proved in §33 for plane Lebesgue measure (§33, Theorems 3–5). The proofs given there carry over verbatim to the general case considered here, and so we shall not repeat them.

THEOREM 4. *The collection $\mathfrak{M}$ of all measurable sets is a ring.*

Proof. Since

$$A_1 \cap A_2 = A_1 \setminus (A_1 \setminus A_2),$$

$$A_1 \cup A_2 = E \setminus [(E \setminus A_1) \cap (E \setminus A_2)],$$

it is sufficient to prove the following. If $A_1, A_2 \in \mathfrak{M}$, then

$$A = A_1 \setminus A_2 \in \mathfrak{M}.$$

Let A_1 and A_2 be measurable; then there exist $B_1, B_2 \in \Re(S_m)$ such that

$$\mu^*(A_1 \triangle B_1) < \epsilon/2, \qquad \mu^*(A_2 \triangle B_2) < \epsilon/2.$$

Setting $B = B_1 \setminus B_2 \in \Re(S_m)$ and using the relation

$$(A_1 \setminus A_2) \triangle (B_1 \setminus B_2) \subseteq (A_1 \triangle B_1) \cup (A_2 \triangle B_2),$$

we obtain

$$\mu^*(A \triangle B) < \epsilon.$$

Hence, A is measurable.

REMARK. It is obvious that E is the unit of the ring $\mathfrak{M}$, so that the latter is an algebra.

THEOREM 5. *The function $\mu(A)$ is additive on the set $\mathfrak{M}$ of measurable sets.*

The proof of this theorem is a verbatim repetition of the proof of Theorem 7, §33.

THEOREM 6. *The function $\mu(A)$ is σ-additive on the set $\mathfrak{M}$ of measurable sets.*

Proof. Let

$$A = \bigcup_{n=1}^{\infty} A_n \qquad (A, A_i \in \mathfrak{M}, \quad A_i \cap A_j = \emptyset \quad \text{if} \quad i \neq j).$$

By Theorem 1,

(1) $$\mu^*(A) \leq \sum_n \mu(A_n),$$

and by Theorem 5, for arbitrary N,

$$\mu^*(A) \geq \mu^*(\textstyle\bigcup_{n=1}^N A_n) = \sum_{n=1}^N \mu^*(A_n).$$

Hence,

(2) $$\mu^*(A) \geq \sum_n \mu(A_n).$$

The theorem follows from (1) and (2).

We have therefore proved that the function $\mu(A)$ defined on $\mathfrak{M}$ possesses all the properties of a σ-additive measure.

This justifies the following

DEFINITION 4. The *Lebesgue extension* $\mu = L(m)$ *of a measure* $m(A)$ is the function $\mu(A)$ defined on the collection $S_\mu = \mathfrak{M}$ of measurable sets and coinciding on this collection with the outer measure $\mu^*(A)$.

In §33, in considering plane Lebesgue measure, we showed that not only finite, but denumerable unions and intersections of measurable sets are measurable. This is also true in the general case, that is,

THEOREM 7. *The collection* $\mathfrak{M}$ *of Lebesgue measurable sets is a Borel algebra with unit* E.

Proof. Since

$$\textstyle\bigcap_n A_n = E \setminus \bigcup_n (E \setminus A_n),$$

and since the complement of a measurable set is measurable, it is sufficient to prove the following: If $A_1, A_2, \cdots, A_n, \cdots \in \mathfrak{M}$, then $A = \bigcup_n A_n \in \mathfrak{M}$. The proof of this assertion is the same as that of Theorem 8, §33, for plane sets.

As in the case of plane Lebesgue measure, the σ-additivity of the measure implies its continuity, that is, if μ is a σ-additive measure defined on a B-algebra, and $A_1 \supseteq A_2 \supseteq \cdots \supseteq A_n \supseteq \cdots$ is a decreasing sequence of measurable sets, with

$$A = \textstyle\bigcap_n A_n,$$

then

$$\mu(A) = \lim_{n \to \infty} \mu(A_n);$$

and if $A_1 \subseteq A_2 \subseteq \cdots \subseteq A_n \subseteq \cdots$ is an increasing sequence of measurable sets, with

$$A = \textstyle\bigcup_n A_n,$$

then

$$\mu(A) = \lim_{n \to \infty} \mu(A_n).$$

The proof of this is the same as that of Theorem 10, §33, for plane measure.

★ 1. From the results of §37 and §38 we easily conclude that every Jordan measurable set A is Lebesgue measurable, and that its Jordan and Lebesgue measures are equal. It follows immediately that the Jordan extension of a σ-additive measure is σ-additive.

2. Every Lebesgue measurable set A is a set of unicity for the initial measure m. In fact, for arbitrary $\epsilon > 0$ there exists a set $B \in \mathfrak{R}$ such that $\mu^*(A \ \Delta \ B) < \epsilon$. For every extension λ of m defined on A,

$$\lambda(B) = m'(B),$$

since the extension of m on $\mathfrak{R} = \mathfrak{R}(S_m)$ is unique. Furthermore,

$$\lambda(A \ \Delta \ B) \leq \mu^*(A \ \Delta \ B) < \epsilon;$$

consequently,

$$|\lambda(A) - m'(B)| < \epsilon.$$

Hence,

$$|\lambda_1(A) - \lambda_2(A)| < 2\epsilon$$

for any two extensions $\lambda_1(A)$, $\lambda_2(A)$ of m. Therefore,

$$\lambda_1(A) = \lambda_2(A).$$

It can be proved that the class of Lebesgue measurable sets includes *all* the sets of unicity of an initial measure m.

3. Let m be a σ-additive measure defined on S, and let $\mathfrak{M} = L(S)$ be the domain of definition of its Lebesgue extension. It easily follows from Theorem 3 of this section that if S_1 is a semi-ring such that

$$S \subseteq S_1 \subseteq \mathfrak{M},$$

then

$$L(S_1) = L(S). \star$$

EXERCISES

1. Show that the collection of subsets A of E for which $\mu(A) = 0$ or $\mu(E \setminus A) = 0$ form a Borel algebra with E as a unit. This algebra is a subalgebra of $\mathfrak{M}$.

2. With the notation of the text for $A \subseteq E$ let

$$\mu_1^*(A) = \sup\{\mu^*(B) : B \subseteq A\}.$$

Show that $\mu_1^*(A) = \mu^*(A)$.

3. Suppose that $A \subseteq E$. Then $A \in \mathfrak{M}$ if, and only if, $A \cap B \in \mathfrak{M}$ for all $B \in S_m$.

4. For $A \subseteq E$, $A \in \mathfrak{M}$ if, and only if, for $\epsilon > 0$ there exist sets B_1, $B_2 \in \mathfrak{M}$ such that $B_1 \subset A \subset B_2$ and $\mu(B_2 \setminus B_1) < \epsilon$. [See §36, Def. 1 (Jordan measurability); also compare with §33, Ex. 6.]

5. For any $A \subseteq E$ we have

     a) $\mu^*(A) = \inf\{\mu B : A \subset B, \ B \in \mathfrak{M}\}$.

     b) $\mu_*(A) = \sup\{\mu B : B \subset A, \ B \in \mathfrak{M}\}$.

We see therefore that (abstract) Lebesgue measure is (abstractly) regular (see §33, Ex. 5).

6. Let S_{m_1}, S_{m_2} be two semi-rings on X with the same unit E; let m_1, m_2 be σ-additive measures defined on S_{m_1}, S_{m_2}, respectively; and let μ_1^*, μ_2^* be the outer measures on the set of all subsets of E defined by using m_1, m_2, respectively. Then $\mu_1^*(A) = \mu_2^*(A)$ for every $A \subseteq E$ if, and only if, $\mu_1^*(A) = m_2(A)$ for $A \in S_{m_2}$ and $\mu_2^*(A) = m_1(A)$ for $A \in S_{m_1}$. (See §36, Theorem 6 for the analogous theorem on Jordan extensions.)

§39. Extension of Lebesgue measures in the general case

If the semi-ring S_m on which the initial measure m is defined has no unit, the discussion of §38 must be modified. Def. 1 of the outer measure is retained, but the outer measure μ^* is now defined only on the collection $S_{\mu*}$ of the sets A for which there exists a covering $\bigcup_n B_n'$ of sets of S_m with a finite sum

$$\sum_n m(B_n).$$

Def. 2 becomes meaningless. The lower measure can also be defined (in several other ways) in the general case, but we shall not do so. It is more expedient at this point to define a measurable set in terms of the condition given in Theorem 3.

DEFINITION 1. A set A is said to be *measurable* if for arbitrary $\epsilon > 0$ there exists a set $B \in \mathfrak{R}(S_m)$ such that $\mu^*(A \triangle B) < \epsilon$.

Theorems 4, 5, 6 and Def. 4 of the preceding section remain true. The existence of a unit was used only in the proof of Theorem 4. To reprove Theorem 4 in the general case, it is necessary to show again that $A_1, A_2 \in \mathfrak{M}$ implies that $A_1 \cup A_2 \in \mathfrak{M}$. The proof of this is carried out in the same way as for $A_1 \setminus A_2$ on the basis of the relation.

$$(A_1 \cup A_2) \triangle (B_1 \cup B_2) \subseteq (A_1 \triangle B_1) \cup (A_2 \triangle B_2).$$

If S_m has no unit, Theorem 7 of §38 changes to

THEOREM 1. *For arbitrary initial measure m the collection* $\mathfrak{M} = S_{L(m)}$ *of Lebesgue measurable sets is a δ-ring; a set* $A = \bigcup_{n=1}^{\infty} A_n$, *where the sets* A_n *are measurable, is measurable if, and only if, the measure* $\mu(\bigcup_{n=1}^{N} A_n)$ *is bounded by a constant independent of N.*

The proof of this theorem is left to the reader.

REMARK. In our exposition the measure is always finite, so that the necessity of the last condition of the theorem is obvious.

Theorem 1 implies the

COROLLARY. *The collection* $\mathfrak{M}_A$ *of all sets* $B \in \mathfrak{M}$ *which are subsets of a fixed set* $A \in \mathfrak{M}$ *is a Borel algebra.* For instance, the collection of all Lebesgue measurable subsets (in the sense of the usual Lebesgue measure $\mu^{(1)}$ on the real line) of an arbitrary closed interval $[a, b]$ is a Borel algebra.

In conclusion we note yet another property of Lebesgue measures.

DEFINITION 2. A measure μ is said to be *complete* if $\mu(A) = 0$ and $A' \subseteq A$ imply that $A' \in S_\mu$.

It is clear that in that case $\mu(A') = 0$. It can be proved without difficulty that the Lebesgue extension of an arbitrary measure is complete. This follows from the fact that $A' \subseteq A$ and $\mu(A) = 0$ imply that $\mu^*(A') = 0$, and from the fact that an arbitrary set C for which $\mu^*(C) = 0$ is measurable, since $\emptyset \in R$ and

$$\mu^*(C \,\Delta\, \emptyset) = \mu^*(C) = 0.$$

★ Let us indicate a connection between the method of constructing the Lebesgue extension of a measure and the method of completing a metric space. To this end, we note that $m'(A \,\Delta\, B)$ can be thought of as the distance between the elements A, B of the ring $\mathfrak{R}(S_m)$. Then $\mathfrak{R}(S_m)$ becomes a metric space (in general, not complete) and its completion, according to Theorem 3 of §38, consists precisely of all the measurable sets. (In this connection, however, the sets A and B are not distinct, as points of a metric space, if $\mu(A \,\Delta\, B) = 0$.) ★

EXERCISES

1. With the notation of the last paragraph of this section show that μ is a continuous function on the metric space $\mathfrak{M}$.

Chapter VI

MEASURABLE FUNCTIONS

§40. Definition and fundamental properties of measurable functions

Let X and Y be two sets and suppose that $\mathfrak{S}$ and $\mathfrak{S}'$ are classes of subsets of X, Y, respectively. An abstract function $y = f(x)$ defined on X, with values in Y, is said to be $(\mathfrak{S}, \mathfrak{S}')$-*measurable* if $A \in \mathfrak{S}'$ implies that $f^{-1}(A) \in \mathfrak{S}$.

For instance, if both X and Y are the real line D^1 (so that $f(x)$ is a real-valued function of a real variable), and $\mathfrak{S}$, $\mathfrak{S}'$ are the systems of all open (or closed) subsets of D^1, then the above definition of measurable function reduces to the definition of continuous function (see §12). If $\mathfrak{S}$ and $\mathfrak{S}'$ are the collections of all Borel sets, then the definition is that of B-measurable (Borel measurable) functions.

In the sequel our main interest in measurable functions will be from the point of view of integration. Fundamental to this point of view is the concept of the μ-measurability of real functions defined on a set X, with $\mathfrak{S}$ the collection of all μ-measurable subsets of X, and $\mathfrak{S}'$ the class of all B-sets on the real line. For simplicity, we shall assume that X is the unit of the domain of definition S_μ of the measure μ. Since, in view of the results of §38, every σ-additive measure can be extended to a Borel algebra, it is natural to assume that S_μ is a Borel algebra to begin with. Hence, for real functions we formulate the definition of measurability as follows:

DEFINITION 1. *A real function $f(x)$ defined on a set X is said to be μ-measurable if*

$$f^{-1}(A) \in S_\mu$$

for every Borel set A on the real line.

We denote by $\{x : Q\}$ the set of all $x \in X$ with property Q. We have the following

THEOREM 1. *In order that a function $f(x)$ be μ-measurable it is necessary and sufficient that for every real c the set $\{x : f(x) < c\}$ be μ-measurable (that is, that this set be an element of S_μ).*

Proof. The necessity of the condition is obvious, since the half-line $(-\infty, c)$ is a Borel set. To show the sufficiency we note first that the Borel closure $B(\Sigma)$ of the set of all the half-lines $(-\infty, c)$ coincides with the set B^1 of all Borel sets on the real line. By hypothesis, $f^{-1}(\Sigma) \subseteq S_\mu$. But then

$$f^{-1}(B(\Sigma)) = B(f^{-1}(\Sigma)) \subseteq B(S_\mu).$$

However, $B(S_\mu) = S_\mu$, since, by hypothesis, S_μ is a B-algebra. This proves the theorem.

THEOREM 2. *The pointwise limit function of a sequence of μ-measurable functions is μ-measurable.*

Proof. Suppose that $f_n(x) \to f(x)$. Then

(1) $$\{x : f(x) < c\} = \bigcup_k \bigcup_n \bigcap_{m > n} \{x : f_m(x) < c - 1/k\}.$$

For, if $f(x) < c$, there exists a k such that $f(x) < c - 2/k$; furthermore, for this k there is a sufficiently large n such that

$$f_m(x) < c - 1/k$$

for $m \geq n$. This means that x is an element of the set defined by the right-hand side of (1).

Conversely, if x is an element of the right-hand side of (1), then there exists a k such that

$$f_m(x) < c - 1/k$$

for all sufficiently large m. But then $f(x) < c$, that is, x belongs to the set on the left-hand side of (1).

If the functions $f_n(x)$ are measurable, the sets

$$\{x : f_m(x) < c - 1/k\}$$

are elements of S_μ. Since S_μ is a Borel algebra, the set

$$\{x : f(x) < c\}$$

also belongs to S_μ in virtue of (1). This proves that $f(x)$ is measurable.

For the further discussion of measurable functions it is convenient to represent each such function as the limit of a sequence of simple functions.

DEFINITION 2. A function $f(x)$ is said to be *simple* if it is μ-measurable and if it assumes no more than a countable set of values.

It is clear that the concept of simple function depends on the choice of the measure μ.

The structure of simple functions is characterized by the following theorem:

THEOREM 3. *A function $f(x)$ which assumes no more than a countable set of distinct values*

$$y_1, \cdots, y_n, \cdots$$

is μ-measurable if, and only if, all the sets

$$A_n = \{x : f(x) = y_n\}$$

are μ-measurable.

Proof. The necessity of the condition is clear, since each A_n is the inverse image of a set consisting of one point y_n, and every such set is a Borel set. The sufficiency follows from the fact that, by hypothesis, the inverse image $f^{-1}(B)$ of an arbitrary set $B \subseteq D^1$ is the union $\bigcup_{y_n \in B} A_n$ of no more than a countable number of measurable sets A_n, that is, it is measurable.

The further use of simple functions will be based on the following theorem:

THEOREM 4. *In order that a function $f(x)$ be μ-measurable it is necessary and sufficient that it be representable as the limit of a uniformly convergent sequence of simple functions.*

Proof. The sufficiency is clear from Theorem 2. To prove the necessity we consider an arbitrary measurable function $f(x)$ and set $f_n(x) = m/n$, where $m/n \leq f(x) < (m + 1)/n$ (m an integer, n a natural number). It is clear that the functions $f_n(x)$ are simple; they converge uniformly to $f(x)$ as $n \to \infty$, since $|f(x) - f_n(x)| \leq 1/n$.

THEOREM 5. *The sum of two μ-measurable functions is μ-measurable.*

Proof. We prove the theorem first for simple functions. If $f(x)$ and $g(x)$ are two simple functions assuming the values

$$f_1, \cdots, f_n, \cdots,$$

$$g_1, \cdots, g_n, \cdots,$$

respectively, then their sum $f(x) + g(x)$ can assume only the values $h = f_i + g_j$, where each of these values is assumed on the set

$$(2) \qquad \{x : h(x) = h\} = \bigcup_{f_i + g_j = h} (\{x : f(x) = f_i\} \cap \{x : g(x) = g_j\}).$$

The possible number of values of h is countable, and the corresponding set $\{x : h(x) = h\}$ is measurable, since the right side of (2) is obviously a measurable set.

To prove the theorem for arbitrary measurable functions $f(x)$ and $g(x)$ we consider sequences of simple functions $\{f_n(x)\}$ and $\{g_n(x)\}$ converging to $f(x)$ and $g(x)$, respectively. Then the simple functions $f_n(x) + g_n(x)$ converge uniformly to the function $f(x) + g(x)$. The latter, in view of Theorem 4, is measurable.

THEOREM 6. *A B-measurable function of a μ-measurable function is μ-measurable.*

Proof. Let $f(x) = \varphi[\psi(x)]$, where φ is Borel measurable and ψ is μ-measurable. If $A \subseteq D^1$ is an arbitrary B-measurable set, then its inverse image $A' = \varphi^{-1}(A)$ is B-measurable, and the inverse image $A'' = \psi^{-1}(A')$ of A' is μ-measurable. Since $f^{-1}(A) = A''$, it follows that f is measurable.

Theorem 6 is applicable, in particular, to continuous functions φ (they are always B-measurable).

THEOREM 7. *The product of μ-measurable functions is μ-measurable.*

Proof. Since $fg = \frac{1}{4}[(f + g)^2 - (f - g)^2]$, the theorem follows from Theorems 5 and 6 and the fact that $\varphi(t) = t^2$ is continuous.

EXERCISE. Show that if $f(x)$ is measurable and nonvanishing, then $1/f(x)$ is also measurable.

In the study of measurable functions it is often possible to neglect the values of the function on a set of measure zero. In this connection, we introduce the following

DEFINITION. Two functions f and g defined on the same measurable set E are said to be *equivalent* (notation: $f \sim g$) if

$$\mu\{x : f(x) \neq g(x)\} = 0.$$

We say that a property is satisfied *almost everywhere* (abbreviated a.e.) on E if it is satisfied at all points of E except for a set of measure zero. Hence, two functions are equivalent if they are equal a.e.

THEOREM 8. *If two functions f and g, continuous on a closed interval E, are equivalent, they are equal.*

Proof. Let us suppose that $f(x_0) \neq g(x_0)$, i.e., $f(x_0) - g(x_0) \neq 0$. Since $f - g$ is continuous, $f - g$ does not vanish in some neighborhood of x_0. This neighborhood has positive measure; hence

$$\mu\{x : f(x) \neq g(x)\} > 0,$$

that is, the continuous functions f and g cannot be equivalent if they differ even at a single point.

Obviously, the equivalence of two arbitrary measurable (that is, in general, discontinuous) functions does not imply their equality; for instance, the function equal to 1 at the rational points and 0 at the irrational points is equivalent to the function identically zero on the real line.

THEOREM 9. *A function $f(x)$ defined on a measurable set E and equivalent on E to a measurable function $g(x)$ is measurable.*

In fact, it follows from the definition of equivalence that the sets

$$\{x : f(x) > a\}, \qquad \{x : g(x) > a\}$$

may differ only on a set of measure zero; consequently, if the second set is measurable, so is the first.

★ The above definition of a measurable function is quite formal. In 1913 Luzin proved the following theorem, which shows that a measurable function is a function which in a certain sense can be approximated by a continuous function.

LUZIN'S THEOREM. *In order that a function $f(x)$ be measurable on a closed interval $[a, b]$ it is necessary and sufficient that for every $\epsilon > 0$ there exist a* *function $\varphi(x)$ continuous on $[a, b]$ such that*

$$\mu\{x:f(x) \neq \varphi(x)\} \leq \epsilon.$$

In other words, a measurable function can be made into a continuous function by changing its values on a set of arbitrarily small measure. This property, called by Luzin the C-property, may be taken as the definition of a measurable function.★

EXERCISES

1. For $A \subseteq X$ let χ_A be the characteristic function of A defined by $\chi_A(x) = 1$ if $x \in A$, $\chi_A(x) = 0$ if $x \in X \setminus A$.

a) $\chi_{A \cap B}(x) = \chi_A(x)\chi_B(x)$,

$\chi_{A \cup B}(x) = \chi_A(x) + \chi_B(x) - \chi_A(x)\chi_B(x)$,

$\chi_{A \triangle B}(x) = |\chi_A(x) - \chi_B(x)|$,

$\chi_\emptyset(x) \equiv 0, \qquad \chi_X(x) \equiv 1$,

$\chi_A(x) \leq \chi_B(x)$ $(x \in X)$ if, and only if, $A \subseteq B$.

b) $\chi_A(x)$ is μ-measurable if, and only if, $A \in S_\mu$.

2. Suppose $f(x)$ is a real-valued function of a real variable. If $f(x)$ is nondecreasing, then $f(x)$ is Borel measurable.

3. Let $X = [a, b]$ be a closed interval on the real line. If $f(x)$ is defined on X and $X = \bigcup_{i=1}^{n} E_i$, where each E_i is a subinterval of X, $E_i \cap E_j = \emptyset$ and $f(E_i) = y_i$, then we call f a *step function*.

Suppose that f is nondecreasing (or nonincreasing) on X. Show that all the functions of the approximating sequence of simple functions $\{f_n\}$ of Theorem 4 of this section are step functions.

4. Assume that $X = [a, b]$ contains a non-Lebesgue measurable set A. Define a function $f(x)$ on X such that $|f(x)|$ is Lebesgue measurable, but $f(x)$ is not.

5. Two real functions $f(x)$ and $g(x)$ defined on a set X are both μ-measurable. Show that $\{x:f(x) = g(x)\}$ is μ-measurable.

6. Let X be a set containing two or more points. Suppose that $\mathfrak{S} = \{\emptyset, X\}$. Describe all measurable functions.

7. Let $f(x)$ be a μ-measurable function defined on X. For t real define $\varphi(t) = \mu(\{x:f(x) < t\})$. Show that φ is monotone nondecreasing, continuous on the left, $\lim_{t \to -\infty} \varphi(t) = 0$, and $\lim_{t \to \infty} \varphi(t) = \mu(X)$. φ is called the *distribution function* of $f(x)$.

§41. Sequences of measurable functions. Various types of convergence

Theorems 5 and 7 of the preceding section show that the arithmetical operations applied to measurable functions again yield measurable functions. According to Theorem 2 of §40, the class of measurable functions, unlike the class of continuous functions, is also closed under passage to a limit. In addition to the usual pointwise convergence, it is expedient to define certain other types of convergence for measurable functions. In this section we shall consider these definitions of convergence, their basic properties and the relations between them.

DEFINITION 1. A sequence of functions $f_n(x)$ defined on a measure space X (that is, a space with a measure defined in it) is said to *converge to a function $F(x)$ a.e.* if

$$(1) \qquad \lim_{n \to \infty} f_n(x) = F(x)$$

for almost all $x \in X$ [that is, the set of x for which (1) does not hold is of measure zero].

EXAMPLE. The sequence of functions $f_n(x) = (-x)^n$ converges to the function $F(x) \equiv 0$ a.e. on the closed interval $[0, 1]$ (indeed, everywhere except at the point $x = 1$).

Theorem 2 of §40 admits of the following generalization.

THEOREM 1. *If a sequence $\{f_n(x)\}$ of μ-measurable functions converges to a function $F(x)$ a.e., then $F(x)$ is measurable.*

Proof. Let A be the set on which

$$\lim_{n \to \infty} f_n(x) = F(x).$$

By hypothesis, $\mu(E \setminus A) = 0$. The function $F(x)$ is measurable on A by Theorem 2 of §40. Since every function is obviously measurable on a set of measure zero, $F(x)$ is measurable on $(E \setminus A)$; consequently, it is measurable on E.

EXERCISE. Suppose that a sequence of measurable functions $f_n(x)$ converges a.e. to a limit function $f(x)$. Prove that the sequence $f_n(x)$ converges a.e. to $g(x)$ if, and only if, $g(x)$ is equivalent to $f(x)$.

The following theorem, known as Egorov's theorem, relates the notions of convergence a.e. and uniform convergence.

THEOREM 2. *Suppose that a sequence of measurable functions $f_n(x)$ converges to $f(x)$ a.e. on E. Then for every $\delta > 0$ there exists a measurable set $E_\delta \subset E$ such that*

1) $\mu(E_\delta) > \mu(E) - \delta$;

2) *the sequence $f_n(x)$ converges to $f(x)$ uniformly on E_δ.*

Proof. According to Theorem 1, $f(x)$ is measurable. Set

$$E_n{}^m = \bigcap_{i \geq n} \{x : |f_i(x) - f(x)| < 1/m\}.$$

Hence, $E_n{}^m$ for fixed m and n is the set of all x for which

$$|f_i(x) - f(x)| < 1/m \qquad\qquad (i \geq n).$$

Let

$$E^m = \bigcup_n E_n{}^m.$$

It is clear from the definition of the sets $E_n{}^m$ that

$$E_1{}^m \subseteq E_2{}^m \subseteq \cdots \subseteq E_n{}^m \subseteq \cdots$$

for fixed m. Therefore, since a σ-additive measure is continuous (see §38), for arbitrary m and $\delta > 0$ there exists an $n(m)$ such that

$$\mu(E^m \setminus E_{n(m)}{}^m) < \delta/2^m.$$

We set

$$E_\delta = \bigcap_m E_{n(m)}{}^m$$

and prove that E_δ is the required set.

We shall prove first that the sequence $\{f_i(x)\}$ converges uniformly to $f(x)$ on E_δ. This follows at once from the fact that if $x \in E_\delta$, then

$$|f_i(x) - f(x)| < 1/m \qquad\qquad (i \geq n(m))$$

for arbitrary m. We now estimate the measure of the set $E \setminus E_\delta$. To do so we note that $\mu(E \setminus E^m) = 0$ for every m. In fact, if $x_0 \in E \setminus E^m$, then

$$|f_i(x_0) - f(x_0)| \geq 1/m$$

for infinitely many values of i, that is, the sequence $\{f_n(x)\}$ does not converge to $f(x)$ at $x = x_0$. Since $\{f_n(x)\}$ converges to $f(x)$ a.e. by hypothesis,

$$\mu(E \setminus E^m) = 0.$$

Hence,

$$\mu(E \setminus E_{n(m)}{}^m) = \mu(E^m \setminus E_{n(m)}{}^m) < \delta/2^m.$$

Therefore,

$$\begin{aligned}
\mu(E \setminus E_\delta) &= \mu(E \setminus \bigcap_m E_{n(m)}{}^m) \\
&= \mu(\bigcup_m (E \setminus E_{n(m)}{}^m)) \\
&\leq \sum_m \mu(E \setminus E_{n(m)}{}^m) \\
&< \sum_{m=1}^\infty \delta/2^m = \delta.
\end{aligned}$$

This proves the theorem.

★ DEFINITION 2. A sequence of measurable functions $f_n(x)$ *converges in measure* to a function $F(x)$ if for every $\sigma > 0$

$$\lim_{n\to\infty} \mu\{x: |f_n(x) - F(x)| \geq \sigma\} = 0.$$

Theorems 3 and 4 below relate the concepts of convergence a.e. and convergence in measure.

THEOREM 3. *If a sequence of measurable functions $f_n(x)$ converges a.e. to a function $F(x)$, then it converges in measure to $F(x)$.*

Proof. Theorem 1 implies that the limit function $F(x)$ is measurable. Let A be the set (of measure zero) on which $f_n(x)$ does not converge to $F(x)$. Furthermore, let

$$E_k(\sigma) = \{x : |f_k(x) - F(x)| \geq \sigma\}, \qquad R_n(\sigma) = \bigcup_{k=n}^{\infty} E_k(\sigma),$$

$$M = \bigcap_{n=1}^{\infty} R_n(\sigma).$$

It is clear that all these sets are measurable. Since

$$R_1(\sigma) \supset R_2(\sigma) \supset \cdots,$$

and because of the continuity of the measure,

$$\mu(R_n(\sigma)) \rightarrow \mu(M) \qquad\qquad (n \rightarrow \infty).$$

We now verify that

(2) $$M \subseteq A.$$

In fact, if $x_0 \notin A$, that is, if

$$\lim_{n\to\infty} f_n(x_0) = F(x_0),$$

then for every $\sigma > 0$ there is an n such that

$$|f_n(x_0) - F(x_0)| < \sigma,$$

that i $x_0 \notin E_n(\sigma)$; hence $x_0 \notin M$.

But since $\mu(A) = 0$, it follows from (2) that $\mu(M) = 0$. Consequently,

$$\mu(R_n(\sigma)) \rightarrow 0 \qquad\qquad (n \rightarrow \infty).$$

Since $E_n(\sigma) \subseteq R_n(\sigma)$, this proves the theorem.

It is easy to see by an example that convergence in measure does not imply convergence a.e. For each natural number k define k functions

$$f_1^{(k)}, \cdots, f_k^{(k)}$$

on the half-open interval $(0, 1]$ as follows:

$$f_i^{(k)}(x) = \begin{cases} 1 & (i-1)/k < x \leq i/k, \\ 0 & \text{for the remaining values of } x. \end{cases}$$

Writing these functions in a sequence yields a sequence which, as is easily verified, converges in measure to zero, but converges nowhere (prove this!).

EXERCISE. Suppose that a sequence of measurable functions $f_n(x)$ converges in measure to a limit function $f(x)$. Prove that the sequence $f_n(x)$ converges in measure to $g(x)$ if, and only if, $g(x)$ is equivalent to $f(x)$.

Although the above example shows that the full converse of Theorem 3 is not true, nevertheless we have the following

THEOREM 4. *Suppose that a sequence of measurable functions $f_n(x)$ converges in measure to $f(x)$. Then the sequence $\{f_n(x)\}$ contains a subsequence $\{f_{n_k}(x)\}$ which converges a.e. to $f(x)$.*

Proof. Let $\epsilon_1, \cdots, \epsilon_n, \cdots$ be a sequence of positive numbers such that

$$\lim_{n \to \infty} \epsilon_n = 0,$$

and suppose that the positive numbers $\eta_1, \cdots, \eta_n, \cdots$ are such that the series

$$\eta_1 + \eta_2 + \cdots$$

converges. We construct a sequence of indices

$$n_1 < n_2 < \cdots$$

as follows: n_1 is a natural number such that

$$\mu\{x : |f_{n_1}(x) - f(x)| \geq \epsilon_1\} < \eta_1$$

(such an n_1 necessarily exists). Then n_2 is chosen so that

$$\mu\{x : |f_{n_2}(x) - f(x)| \geq \epsilon_2\} < \eta_2 \qquad (n_2 > n_1).$$

In general, n_k is a natural number such that

$$\mu\{x : |f_{n_k}(x) - f(x)| \geq \epsilon_k\} < \eta_k \qquad (n_k > n_{k-1}).$$

We shall show that the subsequence $\{f_{n_k}(x)\}$ converges to $f(x)$ a.e. In fact, let

$$R_i = \bigcup_{k=i}^{\infty} \{x : |f_{n_k}(x) - f(x)| \geq \epsilon_k\}, \qquad Q = \bigcap_{i=1}^{\infty} R_i.$$

Since

$$R_1 \supset R_2 \supset R_3 \supset \cdots \supset R_n \supset \cdots,$$

and the measure is continuous, it follows that $\mu(R_i) \to \mu(Q)$.

On the other hand, it is clear that $\mu(R_i) < \sum_{k=i}^{\infty} \eta_k$, whence $\mu(R_i) \to 0$ as $i \to \infty$. Since $\mu(R_i) \to 0$,

$$\mu(Q) = 0.$$

It remains to verify that

$$f_{n_k}(x) \to f(x)$$

for all $x \in E \setminus Q$. Suppose that $x_0 \in E \setminus Q$. Then there is an i_0 such that $x_0 \notin R_{i_0}$. Then

$$x_0 \notin \{x : |f_{n_k}(x) - f(x)| \geq \epsilon_k\}$$

for all $k \geq i_0$, i.e.,

$$|f_{n_k}(x_0) - f(x_0)| < \epsilon_k.$$

Since $\epsilon_k \to 0$ by hypothesis,

$$\lim_{k \to \infty} f_{n_k}(x_0) = f(x_0).$$

This proves the theorem.★

EXERCISES

1. Egorov's theorem does not yield the result that there exists a subset $E_0 \subseteq E$ with $\mu E_0 = 0$ and that the sequence $\{f_n(x)\}$ converges uniformly to $f(x)$ on $E \setminus E_0$. However, prove that there exists a sequence $\{E_i\}$ of measurable subsets of E such that $\mu(E \setminus \bigcup_i E_i) = 0$ and on each E_i the convergence is uniform.

2. Suppose that $\{f_n\}$, f are measurable functions defined on E and for $\epsilon > 0$ there exists a measurable set $F \subseteq E$ such that $\mu F < \epsilon$ and $\{f_n(x)\}$ converges uniformly to $f(x)$ in $E \setminus F$. Show that $\{f_n(x)\}$ converges to $f(x)$ a.e. in E.

3. Let X be the set of positive integers, $\mathfrak{S}$ the class of all subsets of X, and for $A \in \mathfrak{S}$ let $\mu(A)$ be the number of points in A. Note that we are here allowing sets of infinite measure. If χ_n is the characteristic function of $\{1, \cdots, n\}$, then $\chi_n(x)$ converges everywhere to $\chi_X(x) \equiv 1$, but the conclusion of Egorov's theorem does not hold.

4. A sequence of measurable functions $f_n(x)$ is said to be *fundamental in measure* if for every $\sigma > 0$,

$$\lim_{m,n \to \infty} \mu\{x : |f_n(x) - f_m(x)| > \sigma\} = 0.$$

Show that if $\{f_n(x)\}$ is fundamental in measure, then there exists a measurable function $f(x)$ such that $\{f_n(x)\}$ converges in measure to $f(x)$. Hint: Use Theorem 4.

5. Let $\{A_n\}$ be a sequence of measurable sets and let χ_n be the characteristic function of A_n. Show that the sequence $\{\chi_n\}$ is fundamental in measure if, and only if, $\lim_{m,n \to \infty} \mu(A_n \triangle A_m) = 0$.

6. If $\{f_n(x)\}$, $\{g_n(x)\}$ converge in measure to $f(x)$ and $g(x)$, respectively, then $\{f_n(x) + g_n(x)\}$ converges in measure to $f(x) + g(x)$.

Chapter VII

THE LEBESGUE INTEGRAL

In the preceding chapter we considered the fundamental properties of measurable functions, which are a very broad generalization of continuous functions. The classical definition of the integral, the Riemann integral, is, in general, not applicable to the class of measurable functions. For instance, the well known Dirichlet function (equal to zero at the irrational points and one at the rational points) is obviously measurable, but not Riemann integrable. Therefore, the Riemann integral is not suitable for measurable functions.

The reason for this is perfectly clear. For simplicity, let us consider functions on a closed interval. To define the Riemann integral we divide the interval on which a function $f(x)$ is defined into small subintervals and, choosing a point ξ_k in each of these subintervals, form the sum

$$\sum_k f(\xi_k)\Delta x_k .$$

What we do, essentially, is to replace the value of $f(x)$ at each point of the closed interval $\Delta x_k = [x_k , x_{k+1}]$ by its value at an arbitrarily chosen point ξ_k of this interval. But this, of course, can be done only if the values of $f(x)$ at points which are close together are also close together, i.e., if $f(x)$ is continuous or if its set of discontinuities is "not too large." (A bounded function is Riemann integrable if, and only if, its set of discontinuities has measure zero.)

The basic idea of the Lebesgue integral, in contrast to the Riemann integral, is to group the points x not according to their nearness to each other on the x-axis, but according to the nearness of the values of the function at these points. This at once makes it possible to extend the notion of integral to a very general class of functions.

In addition, a single definition of the Lebesgue integral serves for functions defined on arbitrary measure spaces, while the Riemann integral is introduced first for functions of one variable, and is then generalized, with appropriate changes, to the case of several variables.

In the sequel, without explicit mention, we consider a σ-additive measure $\mu(A)$ defined on a Borel algebra with unit X. The sets $A \subseteq X$ of the algebra are μ-measurable, and the functions $f(x)$—defined for all $x \in X$—are also μ-measurable.

§42. The Lebesgue integral of simple functions

We introduce the Lebesgue integral first for the simple functions, that is, for measurable functions whose set of values is countable.

Let $f(x)$ be a simple function with values

$$y_1, \cdots, y_n, \cdots \qquad (y_i \neq y_j \text{ for } i \neq j).$$

It is natural to define the integral of $f(x)$ over (on) a set A as

$$(1) \qquad \int_A f(x) \, d\mu = \sum_n y_n \mu\{x : x \in A, f(x) = y_n\}.$$

We therefore arrive at the following definition.

DEFINITION. A simple function $f(x)$ is μ-*integrable* over A if the series (1) is absolutely convergent. If $f(x)$ is integrable, the sum of the series (1) is called the *integral* of $f(x)$ over A.

In this definition it is assumed that all the y_n are distinct. However, it is possible to represent the value of the integral of a simple function as a sum of products $c_k \mu(B_k)$ without assuming that all the c_k are distinct. This can be done by means of the

LEMMA. *Suppose that* $A = \bigcup_k B_k$, $B_i \cap B_j = \emptyset$ $(i \neq j)$ *and that* $f(x)$ *assumes only one value on each set* B_k. *Then*

$$(2) \qquad \int_A f(x) \, d\mu = \sum_k c_k \mu(B_k),$$

where the function $f(x)$ *is integrable over* A *if, and only if, the series* (2) *is absolutely convergent.*

Proof. It is easy to see that each set

$$A_n = \{x : x \in A, f(x) = y_n\}$$

is the union of all the sets B_k for which $c_k = y_n$. Therefore,

$$\sum_n y_n \mu(A_n) = \sum_n y_n \sum_{c_k = y_n} \mu(B_k) = \sum_k c_k \mu(B_k).$$

Since the measure is nonnegative,

$$\sum_n |y_n| \, \mu(A_n) = \sum_n |y_n| \sum_{c_k = y_n} \mu(B_k) = \sum_k |c_k| \, \mu(B_k),$$

that is, the series $\sum y_n \mu(A_n)$ and $\sum_k c_k \mu(B_k)$ are either both absolutely convergent or both divergent.

We shall now derive some properties of the Lebesgue integral of simple functions.

$$\text{A)} \qquad \int_A f(x) \, d\mu + \int_A g(x) \, d\mu = \int_A \{f(x) + g(x)\} \, d\mu,$$

where the existence of the integrals on the left side implies the existence of the integral on the right side.

To prove A) we assume that $f(x)$ assumes the values f_i on the sets

$F_i \subseteq A$, and that $g(x)$ assumes the values g_j on the sets $G_j \subseteq A$; hence

$$(3) \qquad\qquad J_1 = \int_A f(x)\, d\mu = \sum_i f_i \mu(F_i),$$

$$(4) \qquad\qquad J_2 = \int_A g(x)\, d\mu = \sum_j g_j \mu(G_j).$$

Then, by the lemma,

$$(5) \qquad J = \int_A \{f(x) + g(x)\}\, d\mu = \sum_i \sum_j (f_i + g_j)\mu(F_i \cap G_j).$$

But

$$\mu(F_i) = \sum_j \mu(F_i \cap G_j),$$
$$\mu(G_j) = \sum_i \mu(F_i \cap G_j),$$

so that the absolute convergence of the series (3) and (4) implies the absolute convergence of the series (5). Hence

$$J = J_1 + J_2 .$$

B) For every constant k,

$$k \int_A f(x)\, d\mu = \int_A \{kf(x)\}\, d\mu,$$

where the existence of the integral on the left implies the existence of the integral on the right. (The proof is immediate.)

C) A simple function $f(x)$ bounded on a set A is integrable over A, and

$$\left| \int_A f(x)\, d\mu \right| \leq M\mu(A),$$

where $|f(x)| \leq M$ on A. (The proof is immediate.)

EXERCISES

1. If A, B are measurable subsets of X, then

$$\int_X |\chi_A(x) - \chi_B(x)|\, d\mu = \mu(A \,\Delta\, B).$$

2. If the simple function $f(x)$ is integrable over A and $B \subseteq A$, then $f(x)$ is integrable over B.

3. Let $F_0 = [0, 1]$. Define the simple function $f(x)$ on F_0 as follows: On the 2^{n-1} open intervals deleted in the nth stage of the construction of the Cantor set F let $f(x) = n$. On F let $f(x) = 0$. Compute $\int_{F_0} f(x)\, d\mu$, where μ is linear Lebesgue measure.

§43. The general definition and fundamental properties of the Lebesgue integral

DEFINITION. We shall say that a function $f(x)$ is *integrable* over a set A if there exists a sequence of simple functions $f_n(x)$ integrable over A and uniformly convergent to $f(x)$. The limit

$$(1) \qquad J = \lim_{n\to\infty} \int_A f_n(x) \, d\mu$$

is denoted by

$$\int_A f(x) \, d\mu$$

and is called the integral of $f(x)$ over A.

This definition is correct if the following conditions are satisfied:

1. The limit (1) for an arbitrary uniformly convergent sequence of simple functions integrable over A exists.

2. This limit, for fixed $f(x)$, is independent of the choice of the sequence $\{f_n(x)\}$.

3. For simple functions this definition of integrability and of the integral is equivalent to that of §42.

All these conditions are indeed satisfied.

To prove the first it is enough to note that because of Properties A), B) and C) of integrals of simple functions,

$$\left| \int_A f_n(x) \, d\mu - \int_A f_m(x) \, d\mu \right| \leq \mu(A) \sup \{ |f_n(x) - f_m(x)| ; x \in A \}.$$

To prove the second condition it is necessary to consider two sequences $\{f_n(x)\}$ and $\{f_n^*(x)\}$ and to use the fact that

$$\left| \int_A f_n(x) \, d\mu - \int_A f_n^*(x) \, d\mu \right|$$

$$\leq \mu(A)\{\sup [|f_n(x) - f(x)| ; x \in A] + \sup [|f_n^*(x) - f(x)| ; x \in A]\}.$$

Finally, to prove the third condition it is sufficient to consider the sequence $f_n(x) = f(x)$.

We shall derive the fundamental properties of the Lebesgue integral.

THEOREM 1.

$$\int_A 1 \cdot d\mu = \mu(A).$$

Proof. This is an immediate consequence of the definition.

THEOREM 2. *For every constant k,*

$$k \int_A f(x) \, d\mu = \int_A \{kf(x)\} \, d\mu,$$

where the existence of the integral on the left implies the existence of the integral on the right.

Proof. To prove this take the limit in Property B) for simple functions.

THEOREM 3.

$$\int_A f(x) \, d\mu + \int_A g(x) \, d\mu = \int_A \{f(x) + g(x)\} \, d\mu,$$

where the existence of the integrals on the left implies the existence of the integral on the right.

The proof is obtained by passing to the limit in Property A) of integrals of simple functions.

THEOREM 4. *A function $f(x)$ bounded on a set A is integrable over A.*

The proof is carried out by passing to the limit in Property C).

THEOREM 5. *If $f(x) \geq 0$, then*

$$\int_A f(x) \, d\mu \geq 0,$$

on the assumption that the integral exists.

Proof. For simple functions the theorem follows immediately from the definition of the integral. In the general case, the proof is based on the possibility of approximating a nonnegative function by simple functions (in the way indicated in the proof of Theorem 4, §40).

COROLLARY 1. *If $f(x) \geq g(x)$, then*

$$\int_A f(x) \, d\mu \geq \int_A g(x) \, d\mu.$$

COROLLARY 2. *If $m \leq f(x) \leq M$ on A, then*

$$m\mu(A) \leq \int_A f(x) \, d\mu \leq M\mu(A).$$

THEOREM 6. *If*

$$A = \bigcup_n A_n \qquad (A_i \cap A_j = \emptyset \text{ for } i \neq j),$$

then

$$\int_A f(x) \, d\mu = \sum_n \int_{A_n} f(x) \, d\mu,$$

where the existence of the integral on the left implies the existence of the integrals and the absolute convergence of the series on the right.

Proof. We first verify the theorem for a simple function $f(x)$ which assumes the values

$$y_1, \cdots, y_k, \cdots.$$

Let

$$B_k = \{x : x \in A, f(x) = y_k\},$$
$$B_{nk} = \{x : x \in A_n, f(x) = y_k\}.$$

Then

(1)
$$\int_A f(x)\, d\mu = \sum_k y_k \mu(B_k) = \sum_k y_k \sum_n \mu(B_{nk})$$
$$= \sum_n \sum_k y_k \mu(B_{nk}) = \sum_n \int_{A_n} f(x)\, d\mu.$$

Since the series $\sum_k y_k \mu(B_k)$ is absolutely convergent if $f(x)$ is integrable, and the measures are nonnegative, all the other series in (1) also converge absolutely.

If $f(x)$ is an arbitrary function, its integrability over A implies that for every $\epsilon > 0$ there exists a simple function $g(x)$ integrable over A such that

(2)
$$|f(x) - g(x)| < \epsilon.$$

For $g(x)$,

(3)
$$\int_A g(x)\, d\mu = \sum_n \int_{A_n} g(x)\, d\mu,$$

where $g(x)$ is integrable over each of the sets A_n, and the series in (3) is absolutely convergent. The latter and the estimate (2) imply that $f(x)$ is also integrable over each A_n, and

$$\sum_n \left| \int_{A_n} f(x)\, d\mu - \int_{A_n} g(x)\, d\mu \right| \leq \sum_n \epsilon\mu(A_n) \leq \epsilon\mu(A),$$

$$\left| \int_A f(x)\, d\mu - \int_A g(x)\, d\mu \right| \leq \epsilon\mu(A).$$

This together with (3) yields the absolute convergence of the series

$$\sum_n \int_{A_n} f(x)\, d\mu$$

and the estimate

$$\left| \sum_n \int_{A_n} f(x)\, d\mu - \int_A f(x)\, d\mu \right| \leq 2\epsilon\mu(A).$$

Since $\epsilon > 0$ is arbitrary,

$$\sum_n \int_{A_n} f(x) \, d\mu = \int_A f(x) \, d\mu.$$

COROLLARY. *If $f(x)$ is integrable over A, then $f(x)$ is integrable over an arbitrary $A' \subseteq A$.*

THEOREM 7. *If a function $\varphi(x)$ is integrable over A, and $|f(x)| \leq \varphi(x)$, then $f(x)$ is also integrable over A.*

Proof. If $f(x)$ and $\varphi(x)$ are simple functions, then A can be written as the union of a countable number of sets on each of which $f(x)$ and $\varphi(x)$ are constant:

$$f(x) = a_n, \qquad \varphi(x) = \alpha_n \qquad\qquad (\,|a_n| \leq \alpha_n).$$

The integrability of $\varphi(x)$ implies that

$$\sum_n |a_n| \, \mu(A_n) \leq \sum_n \alpha_n \mu(A_n) = \int_A \varphi(x) \, d\mu.$$

Therefore $f(x)$ is also integrable, and

$$\left| \int_A f(x) \, d\mu \right| = |\sum_n a_n \mu(A_n)| \leq \sum_n |a_n| \, \mu(A_n)$$

$$= \int_A |f(x)| \, d\mu \leq \int_A \varphi(x) \, d\mu.$$

Passage to the limit proves the theorem in the general case.

TRANS. NOTE. The proof is as follows: For $\epsilon > 0$, choose an $n_0 > 1/\epsilon$. Let $\{\varphi_n : n \geq n_0\}$ be a sequence of integrable simple functions converging uniformly to the function $\varphi(x) + \epsilon$, and let $\{f_n : n \geq n_0\}$ be a sequence of simple functions converging uniformly to $f(x)$. These sequences are chosen so that they satisfy the inequalities

$$\varphi_n(x) \geq 0, \qquad |\varphi_n(x) - [\varphi(x) + \epsilon]| < 1/n, \qquad |f_n(x) - f(x)| < 1/n.$$

Then $|f_n(x)| < \varphi_n(x)$ and

$$\left| \int_A f_n(x) \, d\mu \right| \leq \int_A |f_n(x)| \, d\mu \leq \int_A \varphi_n(x) \, d\mu.$$

Since

$$\int_A \varphi_n(x) \, d\mu \to \int_A \varphi(x) \, d\mu + \epsilon\mu(A),$$

each $f_n(x)$ is integrable and $f(x)$ is integrable, and

$$\left| \int_A f(x) \, d\mu \right| \leq \int_A \varphi(x) \, d\mu + \epsilon\mu(A).$$

Since $\epsilon > 0$ is arbitrary, the desired inequality follows.

THEOREM 8. *The integrals*

$$J_1 = \int_A f(x) \, d\mu, \qquad J_2 = \int_A |f(x)| \, d\mu$$

either both exist or both do not exist.

Proof. The existence of J_2 implies the existence of J_1 by Theorem 7. For a simple function the converse follows from the definition of the integral. The general case is proved by passing to the limit and noting that

$$||a| - |b|| \leq |a - b|.$$

THEOREM 9 (THE CHEBYSHEV INEQUALITY). *If* $\varphi(x) \geq 0$ *on* A, *then*

$$\mu\{x : x \in A, \quad \varphi(x) \geq c\} \leq (1/c) \int_A \varphi(x) \, d\mu.$$

Proof. Setting

$$A' = \{x : x \in A, \varphi(x) \geq c\},$$

we have

$$\int_A \varphi(x) \, d\mu = \int_{A'} \varphi(x) \, d\mu + \int_{A \setminus A'} \varphi(x) \, d\mu \geq \int_{A'} \varphi(x) \, d\mu \geq c\mu(A').$$

COROLLARY. *If*

$$\int_A |f(x)| \, d\mu = 0,$$

then $f(x) = 0$ *a.e.*

For, by the Chebyshev inequality,

$$\mu\{x : x \in A, |f(x)| \geq 1/n\} \leq n \int_A |f(x)| \, d\mu = 0$$

for all n. Therefore,

$$\mu\{x : x \in A, f(x) \neq 0\} \leq \sum_{n=1}^{\infty} \mu\{x : x \in A, |f(x)| \geq 1/n\} = 0.$$

EXERCISES

1. Suppose $f(x)$ is integrable over E, and that F is a measurable subset of E. Then $\chi_F f$ is integrable over E and

$$\int_E \chi_F(x) f(x) \, d\mu = \int_F f(x) \, d\mu.$$

2 (FIRST MEAN VALUE THEOREM). Let $f(x)$ be measurable,

$$m \leq f(x) \leq M$$

on A, and suppose that $g(x) \geq 0$ is integrable over A. Then there exists a real number a such that $m \leq a \leq M$ and $\int_A f(x)g(x) \, d\mu = a \int_A g(x) \, d\mu$.

3. Suppose that $f(x)$ is integrable over the set $E = [a, b]$ and that μ is linear Lebesgue measure. Then $F(x) = \int_{[a,x]} f(x) \, d\mu$ is defined for $a \leq x \leq b$.

    a) Show that

$$[F(x_2) - F(x_1)]/(x_2 - x_1) = [1/(x_2 - x_1)] \int_{[x_1,x_2]} f(x) \, d\mu$$

for $a \leq x_1 < x_2 \leq b$.

    b) For any point x_0, $a < x_0 < b$, at which $f(x)$ is continuous show that $F'(x_0) = f(x_0)$.

4. Let f, g be integrable over E.

    a) If $\int_A f(x) \, d\mu = \int_A g(x) \, d\mu$ for every measurable $A \subseteq E$, then $f(x) = g(x)$ a.e. on E.

    b) If $\int_A f(x) \, d\mu = 0$, for every measurable $A \subseteq E$, then $f(x) = 0$ a.e. on E.

5. Suppose $E = [a, b]$, μ is Lebesgue measure and f is integrable over E. Show that $\int_{[a,c]} f(x) \, d\mu = 0$ for $a \leq c \leq b$ implies that $f(x) = 0$ a.e. on E. Hint: Consider the class $\mathfrak{S}$ of $A \subseteq E$ for which $\int_A f(x) \, d\mu = 0$ and apply the preceding exercise.

§44. Passage to the limit under the Lebesgue integral

The question of taking the limit under the integral sign, or, equivalently, the possibility of termwise integration of a convergent series often arises in various problems.

It is proved in classical analysis that a sufficient condition for interchanging limits in this fashion is the uniform convergence of the sequence (or series) involved.

In this section we shall prove a far-reaching generalization of the corresponding theorem of classical analysis.

THEOREM 1. *If a sequence $f_n(x)$ converges to $f(x)$ on A and*

$$|f_n(x)| \leq \varphi(x)$$

for all n, where $\varphi(x)$ is integrable over A, then the limit function $f(x)$ is in-

tegrable over A and

$$\int_A f_n(x) \, d\mu \to \int_A f(x) \, d\mu.$$

Proof. It easily follows from the conditions of the theorem that

$$|f(x)| \le \varphi(x).$$

Let $A_k = \{x : k - 1 \le \varphi(x) < k\}$, and let $B_m = \bigcup_{k \ge m+1} A_k = \{x : \varphi(x) \ge m\}$.
By Theorem 6 of §43,

$$(*) \qquad \int_A \varphi(x) \, d\mu = \sum_k \int_{A_k} \varphi(x) \, d\mu,$$

and the series $(*)$ converges absolutely.
　　Hence

$$\int_{B_m} \varphi(x) \, d\mu = \sum_{k \ge m+1} \int_{A_k} \varphi(x) \, d\mu.$$

The convergence of the series $(*)$ implies that there exists an m such that

$$\int_{B_m} \varphi(x) \, d\mu < \epsilon/5.$$

The inequality $\varphi(x) < m$ holds on $A \setminus B_m$. By Egorov's theorem, $A \setminus B_m$ can be written as $A \setminus B_m = C \cup D$, where $\mu(D) < \epsilon/5m$ and the sequence $\{f_n\}$ converges uniformly to f on C.
　　Choose an N such that

$$|f_n(x) - f(x)| < \epsilon/5\mu(C)$$

for all $n > N$ and $x \in C$. Then

$$\int_A [f_n(x) - f(x)] \, d\mu = \int_{B_m} f_n(x) \, d\mu - \int_{B_m} f(x) \, d\mu$$

$$+ \int_D f_n(x) \, d\mu - \int_D f(x) \, d\mu + \int_C [f_n(x) - f(x)] \, d\mu < 5\epsilon/5 = \epsilon.$$

COROLLARY. *If $|f_n(x)| \le M$ and $f_n(x) \to f(x)$, then*

$$\int_A f_n(x) \, d\mu \to \int_A f(x) \, d\mu.$$

REMARK. Inasmuch as the values assumed by a function on a set of measure zero do not affect the value of the integral, it is sufficient to assume in Theorem 1 that $\{f_n(x)\}$ converges to $f(x)$ a.e.

THEOREM 2. *Suppose that*

$$f_1(x) \leq f_2(x) \leq \cdots \leq f_n(x) \leq \cdots$$

on a set A, where the functions $f_n(x)$ are integrable and their integrals are bounded from above:

$$\int_A f_n(x) \, d\mu \leq K.$$

Then

(1) $f(x) = \lim_{n \to \infty} f_n(x)$

exists a.e. on A, $f(x)$ is integrable on A and

$$\int_A f_n(x) \, d\mu \to \int_A f(x) \, d\mu.$$

Clearly, the theorem also holds for a monotone descending sequence of integrable functions whose integrals are bounded from below.

On the set on which the limit (1) does not exist, $f(x)$ can be defined arbitrarily; for instance, we may set $f(x) = 0$ on this set.

Proof. We assume that $f(x) \geq 0$, since the general case is easily reduced to this case by writing

$$\bar{f}_n(x) = f_n(x) - f_1(x).$$

We consider the set

$$\Omega = \{x : x \in A, f_n(x) \to \infty\}.$$

It is easy to see that $\Omega = \bigcap_r \bigcup_n \Omega_n^{(r)}$, where

$$\Omega_n^{(r)} = \{x : x \in A, f_n(x) > r\}.$$

By the Chebyshev inequality (Theorem 9, §43),

$$\mu(\Omega_n^{(r)}) \leq K/r.$$

Since $\Omega_1^{(r)} \subseteq \Omega_2^{(r)} \subseteq \cdots \subseteq \Omega_n^{(r)} \subseteq \cdots$, it follows that

$$\mu(\bigcup_n \Omega_n^{(r)}) \leq K/r.$$

Further, since

$$\Omega \subseteq \bigcup_n \Omega_n^{(r)}$$

for every r, $\mu(\Omega) \leq K/r$. Since r is arbitrary,

$$\mu(\Omega) = 0.$$

This also proves that the monotone sequence $f_n(x)$ has a finite limit $f(x)$ a.e. on A.

Now let $\varphi(x) = r$ for all x such that

$$r - 1 \leq f(x) < r \qquad\qquad (r = 1, 2, \cdots).$$

If we prove that $\varphi(x)$ is integrable on A, the theorem will follow immediately from Theorem 1.

We denote by A_r the set of all points $x \in A$ for which $\varphi(x) = r$ and set

$$B_s = \bigcup_{r=1}^{s} A_r .$$

Since the functions $f_n(x)$ and $f(x)$ are bounded on B_s and $\varphi(x) \leq f(x) + 1$, it follows that

$$\int_{B_s} \varphi(x) \, d\mu \leq \int_{B_s} f(x) \, d\mu + \mu(A)$$

$$= \lim_{n \to \infty} \int_{B_s} f_n(x) \, d\mu + \mu(A) \leq K + \mu(A).$$

But

$$\int_{B_s} \varphi(x) \, d\mu = \sum_{r=1}^{s} r\mu(A_r).$$

Since the partial sums in the above equation are bounded, the series

$$\sum_{r=1}^{\infty} r\mu(A_r) = \int_{A} \varphi(x) \, d\mu$$

converges. Hence $\varphi(x)$ is integrable on A.

COROLLARY. *If $\psi_n(x) \geq 0$ and*

$$\sum_{n=1}^{\infty} \int_{A} \psi_n(x) \, d\mu < \infty,$$

then the series $\sum_{n=1}^{\infty} \psi_n(x)$ *converges a.e. on A and*

$$\int_{A} \left(\sum_{n=1}^{\infty} \psi_n(x) \right) \, d\mu = \sum_{n=1}^{\infty} \int_{A} \psi_n(x) \, d\mu.$$

THEOREM 3 (FATOU). *If a sequence of measurable nonnegative functions* $\{f_n(x)\}$ *converges a.e. on A to $f(x)$ and*

$$\int_{A} f_n(x) \, d\mu \leq K,$$

then $f(x)$ is integrable on A and

$$\int_{A} f(x) \, d\mu \leq K.$$

Proof. Set

$$\varphi_n(x) = \inf \{f_k(x); \, k \geq n\}.$$

$\varphi_n(x)$ is measurable, since

$$\{x : \varphi_n(x) < c\} = \bigcup_{k \geq n} \{x : f_k(x) < c\}.$$

Furthermore, $0 \leq \varphi_n(x) \leq f_n(x)$, so that $\varphi_n(x)$ is integrable, and

$$\int_A \varphi_n(x) \, d\mu \leq \int_A f_n(x) \, d\mu \leq K.$$

Finally,

$$\varphi_1(x) \leq \varphi_2(x) \leq \cdots \leq \varphi_n(x) \leq \cdots$$

and

$$\lim_{n \to \infty} \varphi_n(x) = f(x) \qquad \text{(a.e.)}.$$

The required result follows by application of the preceding theorem to $\{\varphi_n(x)\}$.

THEOREM 4. *If* $A = \bigcup_n A_n$, $A_i \cap A_j = \emptyset$ $(i \neq j)$ *and the series*

$$(2) \qquad \sum_n \int_{A_n} |f(x)| \, d\mu$$

converges, then $f(x)$ *is integrable on* A *and*

$$\int_A f(x) \, d\mu = \sum_n \int_{A_n} f(x) \, d\mu.$$

What is new here as compared with Theorem 6, §43 is the assertion that the convergence of the series (2) implies the integrability of $f(x)$ on A.

We first prove that the theorem is true for a simple function $f(x)$, which assumes the values f_i on the sets B_i. Setting

$$A_{ni} = A_n \cap B_i,$$

we have

$$\int_{A_n} |f(x)| \, d\mu = \sum_i |f_i| \, \mu(A_{ni}).$$

The convergence of the series (2) implies that the series

$$\sum_n \sum_i |f_i| \, \mu(A_{ni}) = \sum_i |f_i| \, \mu(B_i \cap A)$$

converge.

In view of the convergence of the last series, the integral

$$\int_A f(x) \, d\mu = \sum_i f_i \mu(B_i \cap A)$$

exists.

In the general case, we approximate $f(x)$ by a simple function $\tilde{f}(x)$ so that

(3) $$| f(x) - \tilde{f}(x) | < \epsilon.$$

Then

$$\int_{A_n} | \tilde{f}(x) | \, d\mu \leq \int_{A_n} | f(x) | \, d\mu + \epsilon\mu(A_n).$$

Since the series

$$\sum_n \mu(A_n) = \mu(A)$$

converges, the convergence of (2) implies the convergence of

$$\sum_n \int_{A_n} | \tilde{f}(x) | \, d\mu,$$

that is, in view of what has just been proved, the integrability of the simple function $\tilde{f}(x)$ on A. But then, by (3), $f(x)$ is also integrable on A.

EXERCISES

1. Let $X = [0, 1]$, let μ be linear Lebesgue measure and suppose that $f(x) \geq 0$ is measurable.

a) Suppose $\epsilon_1 > \epsilon_2 > \cdots > \epsilon_n > \cdots$, $\epsilon_n \to 0$ and $f(x)$ integrable over $[\epsilon_n, 1]$. Then f is integrable over $[0, 1]$ if, and only if, $\lim_{n\to\infty} \int_{[\epsilon_n,1]} f(x) \, d\mu$ exists, and in that case

$$\int_{[0,1]} f(x) \, d\mu = \lim_{n\to\infty} \int_{[\epsilon_n,1]} f(x) \, d\mu.$$

(This justifies the remark made at the end of §45.)

2. For $f(x)$ measurable on the measurable set E define

$$S_n = \sum_{k=-\infty}^{\infty} k2^{-n}\mu\{x : k2^{-n} \leq f(x) < (k+1)2^{-n}, x \in E\}, n = 1, 2, \cdots.$$

a) If f is integrable on E, then each S_n is absolutely convergent, $\lim_n S_n$ exists and

$$\int_E f(x) \, d\mu = \lim_{n\to\infty} S_n.$$

b) Conversely, if S_n converges absolutely for some n, then S_n converges absolutely for all n, $f(x)$ is integrable over E and the above equality holds.

c) Let $n = 0$ in a). It follows that

$$S_0 = \sum_k | k | \mu\{x : k \leq f(x) < k + 1\} < \infty.$$

Show consequently that f integrable over E implies that

$$\lim_{m \to \infty} m\mu\{x: |f(x)| \geq m, x \in E\} = 0.$$

Hint: Reduce the problem to the case $f(x) \geq 0$.

3. Let X be measurable, and let (a, b) be an interval of real numbers. Suppose $f(x, t)$ is real-valued for $x \in X$, $t \in (a, b)$ and that it satisfies the following:

(i) For $t \in (a, b)$, $f(x, t)$ is integrable over X.

(ii) $\partial f(x, t)/\partial t$ exists for all $t \in (a, b)$ and there exists a function $S(x)$ integrable over X for which

$$|\partial f(x, t)/\partial t| \leq S(x) \qquad [x \in X, t \in (a, b)].$$

Show that

$$d/dt \int_X f(x, t) \, d\mu = \int_X \partial f(x, t)/\partial t \, d\mu.$$

Hint: For $t_0 \in (a, b)$ the limit defining the derivative can be obtained by using a sequence $\{t_n\}$ in (a, b), $t_n \to t_0$. Apply Theorem 1.

§45. Comparison of the Lebesgue and Riemann integrals

We shall discuss the relation of the Lebesgue integral to the usual Riemann integral. In doing so, we restrict ourselves to the simplest case, linear Lebesgue measure on the real line.

THEOREM. *If the Riemann integral*

$$J = (R) \int_a^b f(x) \, dx$$

exists, then $f(x)$ is Lebesgue integrable on $[a, b]$, and

$$\int_{[a,b]} f(x) \, d\mu = J.$$

Proof. Consider the partition of $[a, b]$ into 2^n subintervals by the points

$$x_k = a + (k/2^n)(b - a)$$

and the Darboux sums

$$\bar{S}_n = (b - a)2^{-n} \sum_{k=1}^{2^n} M_{nk},$$

$$\underline{S}_n = (b - a)2^{-n} \sum_{k=1}^{2^n} m_{nk},$$

where M_{nk} is the least upper bound of $f(x)$ on the interval

$$x_{k-1} \leq x \leq x_k,$$

and m_{nk} is the greatest lower bound of $f(x)$ on the same interval. By definition, the Riemann integral is

$$J = \lim_{n \to \infty} \bar{S}_n = \lim_{n \to \infty} \underline{S}_n .$$

We set

$$\bar{f}_n(x) = M_{nk} \qquad (x_{k-1} \leq x < x_k),$$

$$\underline{f}_n(x) = m_{nk} \qquad (x_{k-1} \leq x < x_k).$$

The functions $\bar{f}_n$ and $\underline{f}_n$ can be extended to the point $x = b$ arbitrarily. It is easily verified that

$$\int_{[a,b]} \bar{f}_n(x) \, d\mu = \bar{S}_n ,$$

$$\int_{[a,b]} \underline{f}_n(x) \, d\mu = \underline{S}_n .$$

Since $\{\bar{f}_n\}$ is a nonincreasing sequence and $\{\underline{f}_n\}$ is a nondecreasing sequence,

$$\bar{f}_n(x) \to \bar{f}(x) \geq f(x),$$

$$\underline{f}_n(x) \to \underline{f}(x) \leq f(x)$$

a.e. By Theorem 2 of §44,

$$\int_{[a,b]} \bar{f}(x) \, d\mu = \lim_{n \to \infty} \bar{S}_n = J = \lim_{n \to \infty} \underline{S}_n = \int_{[a,b]} \underline{f}(x) \, d\mu.$$

Therefore,

$$\int_{[a,b]} |\bar{f}(x) - \underline{f}(x)| \, d\mu = \int_{[a,b]} \{\bar{f}(x) - \underline{f}(x)\} \, d\mu = 0;$$

consequently,

$$\bar{f}(x) - \underline{f}(x) = 0$$

a.e., i.e.,

$$\bar{f}(x) = \underline{f}(x) = f(x),$$

$$\int_{[a,b]} f(x) \, d\mu = \int_{[a,b]} \bar{f}(x) \, d\mu = J .$$

This proves the theorem.

TRANS. NOTE. The following well known characterization of Riemann integrable functions now follows immediately from the preceding theorem and the observation that $f(x)$ is continuous at x if, and only if, $\bar{f}(x) = \underline{f}(x)$:

Let $f(x)$ be bounded on $[a, b]$. Then $f(x)$ is Riemann integrable if, and only if, it is continuous a.e.

It is easy to construct an example of a bounded function which is Lebesgue integrable but not Riemann integrable (for instance, the Dirichlet function mentioned above).

An arbitrary function $f(x)$ for which the Riemann integral

$$\int_{\epsilon}^{1} |f(x)| \, dx$$

approaches a finite limit J as $\epsilon \to 0$ is Lebesgue integrable on $[0, 1]$, and

$$\int_{[0,1]} f(x) \, d\mu = \lim_{\epsilon \to 0} \int_{\epsilon}^{1} f(x) \, dx.$$

(See Ex. 4, §44.)

In this connection it is interesting to note that the improper integrals

$$\int_{0}^{1} f(x) \, dx = \lim_{\epsilon \to 0} \int_{\epsilon}^{1} f(x) \, dx,$$

where

$$\lim_{\epsilon \to 0} \int_{\epsilon}^{1} |f(x)| \, dx = \infty,$$

cannot be taken in the sense of Lebesgue: Lebesgue integration is absolute integration in the sense of Theorem 8, §43.

EXERCISES

1. Let $f(x)$, $g(x)$ be Riemann integrable functions on $[a, b]$. Then $f(x)g(x)$ is Riemann integrable on $[a, b]$. This fact can be proved without the characterization of Riemann integrable functions given in the text, but a direct proof is difficult.

2. A nondecreasing (nonincreasing) real-valued function defined on an interval $[a, b]$ is Riemann integrable on this interval.

3. Show that the function

$$f(x) = d/dx(x^2 \sin 1/x^2) = 2x \sin 1/x^2 - (2/x) \cos 1/x^2$$

is not Lebesgue integrable over $[0, 1]$, although $f(x)$ is continuous on $[\epsilon, 1]$ for every $\epsilon > 0$ and $\lim_{\epsilon \to 0} \int_{\epsilon}^{1} f(x) \, dx$ exists; that is, $f(x)$ is improperly Riemann integrable, the integral being only conditionally convergent. Hint: $|f(x)| \geq (2/x) |\cos 1/x^2| - 2x \geq x^{-1} - 2x$ on each of the intervals $\{(2n + \frac{1}{3})\pi\}^{-\frac{1}{2}} \leq x \leq \{(2n - \frac{1}{3})\pi\}^{-\frac{1}{2}}$.

§46. Products of sets and measures

Theorems on the reduction of double (or multiple) integrals to repeated integrals play an important part in analysis. The fundamental result in the theory of multiple Lebesgue integrals is Fubini's theorem, which we shall prove in §48. We first introduce some auxiliary concepts and results which, however, have an interest independent of Fubini's theorem.

The set Z of ordered pairs (x, y), where $x \in X$, $y \in Y$, is called the *product* of the sets X and Y and is denoted by $X \times Y$. In the same way, the set Z of finite ordered sequences $(x_1, \cdots, x_n)$, where $x_k \in X_k$, is called the product of the sets $X_1, \cdots, X_n$ and is denoted by

$$Z = X_1 \times X_2 \times \cdots \times X_n = \times_{k=1}^{n} X_k .$$

In particular, if

$$X_1 = X_2 = \cdots = X_n = X,$$

the set Z is the nth power of the set X:

$$Z = X^n.$$

For instance, the n-dimensional coordinate space D^n is the nth power of the real line D^1. The unit cube J^n, that is, the set of points of D^n with coordinates satisfying the conditions

$$0 \leq x_k \leq 1 \qquad\qquad (1 \leq k \leq n),$$

is the nth power of the closed unit interval $J^1 = [0, 1]$.

If $\mathfrak{S}_1, \cdots, \mathfrak{S}_n$ are collections of subsets of the sets $X_1, \cdots, X_n$, then

$$\mathfrak{R} = \mathfrak{S}_1 \times \cdots \times \mathfrak{S}_n$$

is the collection of subsets of the set $X = \times_k X_k$ representable in the form

$$A = A_1 \times \cdots \times A_n \qquad\qquad (A_k \in \mathfrak{S}_k).$$

If $\mathfrak{S}_1 = \mathfrak{S}_2 = \cdots = \mathfrak{S}_n = \mathfrak{S}$, then $\mathfrak{R}$ is the nth power of $\mathfrak{S}$:

$$\mathfrak{R} = \mathfrak{S}^n.$$

For instance, the set of all parallelopipeds in D^n is the nth power of the set of closed intervals in D^1.

THEOREM 1. *If $\mathfrak{S}_1, \cdots, \mathfrak{S}_n$ are semi-rings, then $\mathfrak{R} = \times_k \mathfrak{S}_k$ is a semi-ring.*

Proof. In view of the definition of a semi-ring (§34), we must prove that if $A, B \in \mathfrak{R}$, then $A \cap B \in \mathfrak{R}$; and if, moreover, $B \subseteq A$, then $A = \bigcup_{i=1}^{m} C_i$, where $C_1 = B$, $C_i \cap C_j = \emptyset$ $(i \neq j)$ and $C_i \in \mathfrak{R}$ $(1 \leq i \leq m)$.

We shall carry out the proof for $n = 2$.

I) Suppose that $A, B \in \mathfrak{S}_1 \times \mathfrak{S}_2$. Then

$$A = A_1 \times A_2, \qquad A_1 \in \mathfrak{S}_1, \qquad A_2 \in \mathfrak{S}_2;$$
$$B = B_1 \times B_2, \qquad B_1 \in \mathfrak{S}_1, \qquad B_2 \in \mathfrak{S}_2.$$

Hence

$$A \cap B = (A_1 \cap B_1) \times (A_2 \cap B_2),$$

and since

$$A_1 \cap B_1 \in \mathfrak{S}_1, \qquad A_1 \cap B_2 \in \mathfrak{S}_2,$$

it follows that

$$A \cap B \in \mathfrak{S}_1 \times \mathfrak{S}_2.$$

II) Now, on the same assumptions as in I), suppose that $B \subseteq A$. Then

$$B_1 \subseteq A_1, \qquad B_2 \subseteq A_2,$$

and because $\mathfrak{S}_1$ and $\mathfrak{S}_2$ are semi-rings, it follows that

$$A_1 = B_1 \cup B^{(1)} \cup \cdots \cup B_1^{(k)},$$
$$A_2 = B_2 \cup B_2^{(1)} \cup \cdots \cup B_2^{(l)},$$
$$A = A_1 \times A_2 = (B_1 \times B_2) \cup (B_1 \times B_2^{(1)}) \cup \cdots \cup (B_1 \times B_2^{(l)})$$
$$\cup (B_1^{(1)} \times B_2) \cup (B_1^{(1)} \times B_2^{(1)}) \cup \cdots \cup (B_1^{(1)} \times B_2^{(l)})$$
$$\cdots \cdots \cdots \cdots \cdots \cdots \cdots \cdots \cdots \cdots \cdots \cdots \cdots \cdots \cdots \cdots$$
$$\cup (B_1^{(k)} \times B_2) \cup (B_1^{(k)} \times B_2^{(1)}) \cup \cdots \cup (B_1^{(k)} \times B_2^{(l)}).$$

In the last relation the first term is $B_1 \times B_2 = B$ and all the other terms are elements of $\mathfrak{S}_1 \times \mathfrak{S}_2$ (all pairwise disjoint). This proves the theorem.

However, if the $\mathfrak{S}_k$ are rings or Borel rings, it does not follow that $\times_k \mathfrak{S}_k$ is a ring or a Borel ring.

Suppose that the measures

$$\mu_1(A_1), \mu_2(A_2), \cdots, \mu_n(A_n) \qquad (A_k \in \mathfrak{S}_k)$$

are defined on the semi-rings $\mathfrak{S}_1, \cdots, \mathfrak{S}_n$.

We define the measure

$$\mu = \mu_1 \times \mu_2 \times \cdots \times \mu_n$$

on

$$\mathfrak{R} = \mathfrak{S}_1 \times \mathfrak{S}_2 \times \cdots \times \mathfrak{S}_n$$

by the following condition: If $A = A_1 \times \cdots \times A_n$, then

$$\mu(A) = \mu_1(A_1)\mu_2(A_2) \cdots \mu_n(A_n).$$

We must prove that $\mu(A)$ is a measure, that is, that $\mu(A)$ is additive. We do so for $n = 2$. Let

$$A = A_1 \times A_2 = \bigcup B^{(k)}, \qquad B^{(i)} \cap B^{(j)} = \emptyset \qquad (i \neq j),$$

$$B^{(k)} = B_1^{(k)} \times B_2^{(k)}.$$

It was shown in §34 that there are partitions

$$A_1 = \bigcup_m C_1^{(m)}, \qquad A_2 = \bigcup_n C_2^{(n)}$$

such that $B_1^{(k)} = \bigcup_{m \in M(k)} C_1^{(m)}$ and $B_2^{(k)} = \bigcup_{n \in N(k)} C_2^{(n)}$. It is obvious that

$$(1) \qquad \mu(A) = \mu_1(A_1)\mu_2(A_2) = \sum_m \sum_n \mu_1(C_1^{(m)})\mu_2(C_2^{(n)}),$$

$$(2) \qquad \mu(B^{(k)}) = \mu_1(B_1^{(k)})\mu_2(B_2^{(k)}) = \sum_{m \in M(k)} \sum_{n \in N(k)} \mu_1(C_1^{(m)})\mu_2(C_2^{(n)}),$$

where the right side of (1) contains just once all the terms appearing on the right side of (2). Therefore,

$$\mu(A) = \sum_k \mu(B^{(k)}),$$

which was to be proved.

In particular, the additivity of the elementary measures in Euclidean n-space follows from the additivity of the linear measure on the real line.

THEOREM 2. *If the measures μ_1, μ_2, $\cdots$, μ_n are σ-additive, then the measure $\mu_1 \times \cdots \times \mu_n$ is σ-additive.*

Proof. We carry out the proof for $n = 2$. Denote by λ_1 the Lebesgue extension of μ_1. Let $C = \bigcup_{n=1}^{\infty} C_n$, where C and C_n are in $\mathfrak{S}_1 \times \mathfrak{S}_2$, that is,

$$C = A \times B \qquad (A \in \mathfrak{S}_1, \quad B \in \mathfrak{S}_2),$$

$$C_n = A_n \times B_n \qquad (A_n \in \mathfrak{S}_1, \quad B_n \in \mathfrak{S}_2).$$

For $x \in A$ we set

$$f_n(x) = \begin{cases} \mu_2(B_n) & (x \in A_n), \\ 0 & (x \notin A_n). \end{cases}$$

It is easy to see that if $x \in A$,

$$\sum_n f_n(x) = \mu_2(B).$$

Consequently, in view of the Corollary to Theorem 2, §44,

$$\sum_n \int_A f_n(x) \, d\lambda_1 = \int_A \mu_2(B) \, d\mu_1(A) = \mu(C).$$

But

$$\int_A f_n(x) \, d\lambda_1 = \mu_2(B_n)\mu_1(A_n) = \mu(C_n),$$

so that

$$\sum_n \mu(C_n) = \mu(C).$$

The Lebesgue extension of the measure $\mu_1 \times \cdots \times \mu_n$ will be called the product of the measures μ_k and will be denoted by

$$\mu_1 \otimes \cdots \otimes \mu_n = \otimes_k \mu_k .$$

If

$$\mu_1 = \cdots = \mu_n = \mu,$$

we obtain the nth power of the measure μ:

$$\mu^n = \otimes_k \mu_k \qquad\qquad (\mu_k = \mu).$$

For instance, the n-dimensional Lebesgue measure μ^n is the nth power of the linear Lebesgue measure μ^1.

EXERCISES

1. If $\mathfrak{S}_1$ and $\mathfrak{S}_2$ are rings, then the collection of all finite disjoint unions of rectangles, i.e., elements of $\mathfrak{S}_1 \times \mathfrak{S}_2$, is a ring.

2. If $\mathfrak{S}_1$ and $\mathfrak{S}_2$ are rings each containing at least two distinct nonempty sets, then $\mathfrak{S}_1 \times \mathfrak{S}_2$ is not a ring.

3. Let $X = Y = [0, 1]$, let $\mathfrak{M}_1 = \mathfrak{M}_2$ be the collection of Lebesgue measurable sets, and let $\mu_1 = \mu_2$ be linear Lebesgue measure. The product measure $\mu = \mu_1 \times \mu_2$ on $\mathfrak{M}_1 \times \mathfrak{M}_2$ is not complete (see the end of §39). Hint: For $y \in Y$, $\mu(X \times y) = 0$. X contains a nonmeasurable subset M.

§47. The representation of plane measure in terms of the linear measure of sections, and the geometric definition of the Lebesgue integral

Let G be a region in the (x, y)-plane bounded by the verticals $x = a$, $x = b$ and by the curves $y = \varphi(x)$, $y = \psi(x)$.

The area of the region G is

$$V(G) = \int_a^b \{\varphi(x) - \psi(x)\} \, dx,$$

where the difference $\varphi(x_0) - \psi(x_0)$ is equal to the length of the section of the region G by the vertical $x = x_0$. Our problem is to carry over this method of measuring areas to an arbitrary product-measure

$$\mu = \mu_x \otimes \mu_y .$$

We shall assume that the measures μ_x and μ_y, defined on Borel algebras with units X and Y, respectively, are σ-additive and complete (if $B \subseteq A$ and $\mu(A) = 0$, then B is measurable). It was shown previously that all Lebesgue extensions have these properties.

We introduce the following notation:

$$A_x = \{y \colon (x, y) \in A\},$$
$$A_y = \{x \colon (x, y) \in A\}.$$

If X and Y are both real lines (so that $X \times Y$ is the plane), then A_{x_0} is the projection on the Y-axis of the section of the set A with the vertical $x = x_0$.

THEOREM 1. *Under the above assumptions,*

$$\mu(A) = \int_X \mu_y(A_x) \, d\mu_x = \int_Y \mu_x(A_y) \, d\mu_y$$

for an arbitrary μ-measurable set A.

(We note that integration over X actually reduces to integration over the set $\bigcup_y A_y \subset X$, in whose complement the function under the integral sign is zero. Similarly, $\int_Y = \int_B$, where $B = \bigcup_x A_x$.)

Proof. It is clearly sufficient to prove that

$$(1) \qquad\qquad \mu(A) = \int_X \varphi_A(x) \, d\mu_x,$$

where $\varphi_A(x) = \mu_y(A_x)$, since the second part of the theorem is completely analogous to the first. We note that the theorem includes the assertion that the set A_x is μ_y-measurable for almost all x (in the sense of the measure μ_x), and that the function $\varphi_A(x)$ is μ_x-measurable. If this were not so, (1) would have no meaning.

The measure μ, the Lebesgue extension of

$$m = \mu_x \times \mu_y,$$

is defined on the collection S_m of sets of the form

$$A = A_{y_0} \times A_{x_0},$$

where A_{y_0} is μ_x-measurable and A_{x_0} is μ_y-measurable.

Relation (1) is obvious for such sets, since

$$\varphi_A(x) = \begin{cases} \mu_y(A_{x_0}) & (x \in A_{y_0}), \\ 0 & (x \notin A_{y_0}). \end{cases}$$

Relation (1) can be extended without difficulty also to the sets of $\Re(S_m)$, that is, to finite unions of disjoint sets of S_m.

The proof of (1) in the general case is based on the following lemma, which has independent interest for the theory of Lebesgue extensions.

LEMMA. *If A is a μ-measurable set, there exists a set B such that*

$$B = \bigcap_n B_n, \qquad B_1 \supseteq B_2 \supseteq \cdots \supseteq B_n \supseteq \cdots,$$

$$B_n = \bigcup_k B_{nk}, \qquad B_{n1} \subseteq B_{n2} \subseteq \cdots \subseteq B_{nk} \subseteq \cdots,$$

where the sets B_{nk} are elements of $\Re(S_m)$, $A \subseteq B$ and

(2) $$\mu(A) = \mu(B).$$

Proof. The proof is based on the fact that, according to the definition of measurability, for arbitrary n the set A can be included in a union

$$C_n = \bigcup_r \Delta_{nr}$$

of sets Δ_{nr} of S_m such that $\mu(C_n) < \mu(A) + 1/n$.

Setting $B_n = \bigcap_{k=1}^n C_k$, it is easily seen that the sets B_n will have the form $B_n = \bigcup_s \delta_{ns}$, where the sets δ_{ns} are elements of S_m. Finally, putting

$$B_{nk} = \bigcup_{s=1}^k \delta_{ns},$$

we obtain the sets required by the lemma.

Relation (1) is easily extended with the aid of the sets $B_{nk} \in \Re(S_m)$ to the sets B_n and B by means of Theorem 2, §44, since

$$\varphi_{B_n}(x) = \lim_{k\to\infty} \varphi_{B_{nk}}(x), \qquad \varphi_{B_{n1}} \leq \varphi_{B_{n2}} \leq \cdots,$$

$$\varphi_B(x) = \lim_{n\to\infty} \varphi_{B_n}(x), \qquad \varphi_{B_1} \geq \varphi_{B_2} \geq \cdots.$$

If $\mu(A) = 0$, then $\mu(B) = 0$, and

$$\varphi_B(x) = \mu_y(B_x) = 0$$

a.e. Since $A_x \subseteq B_x$, A_x is measurable for almost all x and

$$\varphi_A(x) = \mu_y(A_x) = 0,$$

$$\int \varphi_A(x) \, d\mu_x = 0 = \mu(A).$$

Consequently, relation (1) holds for sets A such that $\mu(A) = 0$. If A is arbitrary, we write it as $A = B \setminus C$, where, in view of (2),

$$\mu(C) = 0.$$

Since (1) holds for B and C, it is easy to see that it also holds for A.

This completes the proof of Theorem 1.

We now consider the special case when Y is the real line, μ_y is linear Lebesgue measure and A is the set of points (x, y) such that

$$(3) \qquad \begin{cases} x \in M, \\ 0 \le y \le f(x), \end{cases}$$

where M is a μ_x-measurable set and $f(x)$ is an integrable nonnegative function. Then

$$\mu_y(A_x) = \begin{cases} f(x) & (x \in M), \\ 0 & (x \in M), \end{cases}$$

$$\mu(A) = \int_M f(x) \, d\mu_x.$$

We have proved the following

THEOREM 2. *The Lebesgue integral of a nonnegative integrable function $f(x)$ is equal to the measure $\mu = \mu_x \otimes \mu_y$ of the set A defined by (3).*

If X is also the real line, the set M a closed interval and the function $f(x)$ Riemann integrable, this theorem reduces to the usual expression for the integral as the area under the graph of the function.

EXERCISES

1. The assumption that $\mu_x(X) < \infty$ and $\mu_y(Y) < \infty$, or more generally that X and Y are countable unions of sets of finite measure cannot be dropped from Theorem 1. Let $X = Y = [0, 1]$, let $\mathfrak{S}_x$ be the class of Lebesgue measurable sets of X, μ_x Lebesgue measure, $\mathfrak{S}_y$ the class of all subsets of Y, $\mu_y(A)$ the number of points in A, $A \subseteq Y$. If $E = \{(x, y) : x = y\}$, show that $\int_X \mu_y(E_x) \, d\mu_x = 1$, but $\int_Y \mu_x(E_y) \, d\mu_y = 0$.

2. Under the hypotheses of Theorem 2, the graph of a nonnegative measurable function, i.e., $\{(x, f(x)) : x \in M\}$, has μ-measure zero.

3. Let $X = Y = [0, 1]$, let $\mu_x = \mu_y$ be linear Lebesgue measure and set $\mu = \mu_x \otimes \mu_y$. Suppose that $A \subseteq X$ is nonmeasurable and that $B \subseteq Y$ is such that $\mu_y(B) = 0$.

a) $\chi_{A \times B}(x, y)$ is μ-measurable.

b) $\chi_{A \times B}(x, y)$ is μ_x-measurable for almost all (but not all) $y \in Y$.

4. If A and B are measurable subsets of $X \times Y$, i.e., $(\mu = \mu_x \otimes \mu_y)$-measurable, and $\mu_y(A_x) = \mu_y(B_x)$ for almost every $x \in X$, then

$$\mu(A) = \mu(B).$$

5. Suppose $v = f(u)$ is a strictly increasing continuous function defined on $[0, \infty)$ with $f(0) = 0$ and $\lim_{u \to \infty} f(u) = \infty$. Then $u = f^{-1}(v) = g(v)$ also has all these properties. Suppose that $0 \le u_0 < \infty$, $0 \le v_0 < \infty$, $U = [0, u_0]$, $V = [0, v_0]$, and $\mu_u = \mu_v$ is linear Lebesgue measure. Let

$$F(u_0) = \int_{[0, u_0]} f(u) \, d\mu_u, \; G(v_0) = \int_{[0, v_0]} g(v) \, d\mu_v.$$

Prove Young's inequality:

$$u_0 v_0 \leq F(u_0) + G(v_0),$$

where the equality holds if, and only if, $v_0 = f(u_0)$, or equivalently

$$u_0 = g(v_0).$$

The result can be demonstrated as follows:

a) Let

$$E_1 = \{(u, v) : 0 \leq v \leq f(u), \quad 0 \leq u \leq u_0\},$$

$$E_2 = \{(u, v) : 0 \leq u \leq g(v), \quad 0 \leq v \leq v_0\},$$

$$I = U \times V, \qquad \mu = \mu_u \otimes \mu_v.$$

Show that $I = (I \cap E_1) \cup (I \cap E_2)$, with $\mu[(I \cap E_1) \cap (I \cap E_2)] = 0$ (use §47, Ex. 2). It follows that

$$\mu I = u_0 v_0 = \mu(I \cap E_1) + \mu(I \cap E_2).$$

b) Show that

$$F(u_0) = \int_U f(u)\, d\mu_u = \int_U \left(\int_{[0, f(u)]} d\mu_v \right) d\mu_u$$

$$\geq \int_U \left(\int_{[0,\, \min\, (v_0, f(u))]} d\mu_v \right) d\mu_u$$

$$= \mu(I \cap E_1)$$

(use §47, Theorem 2).

Similarly, one shows that $G(u_0) \geq \mu(I \cap E_2)$.

The result is now clear.

§48. Fubini's theorem

Consider a triple product

$$(1) \qquad\qquad U = X \times Y \times Z.$$

We shall identify the point

$$(x, y, z) \in U$$

with the points

$$((x, y), z),$$

$$(x, (y, z))$$

of the products

(2)
$$(X \times Y) \times Z,$$

(3)
$$X \times (Y \times Z).$$

We therefore agree to regard the products (1), (2) and (3) as identical. If measures μ_x, μ_y, μ_z are defined on X, Y, Z, then the measure.

$$\mu_u = \mu_x \otimes \mu_y \otimes \mu_z$$

may be defined as

$$\mu_u = (\mu_x \otimes \mu_y) \otimes \mu_z,$$

or as

$$\mu_u = \mu_x \otimes (\mu_y \otimes \mu_z).$$

We omit a rigorous proof of the equivalence of these definitions, although it is not difficult.

We shall apply these general ideas to prove the fundamental theorem of the theory of multiple integrals.

FUBINI'S THEOREM. *Suppose that σ-additive and complete measures μ_x and μ_y are defined on Borel algebras with units X and Y, respectively; further, suppose that*

$$\mu = \mu_x \otimes \mu_y,$$

and that the function $f(x, y)$ is μ-integrable on

$$A = A_{y_0} \times A_{x_0}.$$

Then (see the parenthetical remark on p. 69)

(4)
$$\int_A f(x, y) \, d\mu = \int_X \left(\int_{A_x} f(x, y) \, d\mu_y \right) d\mu_x$$
$$= \int_Y \left(\int_{A_y} f(x, y) \, d\mu_x \right) d\mu_y.$$

Proof. The theorem includes among its assertions the existence of the integrals in parentheses for almost all values of the variables with respect to which the integrals are taken.

We shall prove the theorem first for the case $f(x, y) \geq 0$. To this end consider the triple product

$$U = X \times Y \times D^1,$$

where the third term is the real line, and the product measure

$$\lambda = \mu_x \otimes \mu_y \otimes \mu^1 = \mu \otimes \mu^1,$$

where μ^1 is linear Lebesgue measure.

We define a subset W of U as follows:

$$(x, y, z) \in W$$

if

$$x \in A_{y_0}, \qquad y \in A_{x_0},$$
$$0 \leq z \leq f(x, y).$$

In view of Theorem 2, §47,

$$(5) \qquad \lambda(W) = \int_A f(x, y)\, d\mu.$$

On the other hand, by Theorem 1, §47,

$$(6) \qquad \lambda(W) = \int_X \xi(W_x)\, d\mu_x,$$

where $\xi = \mu_y \otimes \mu^1$ and W_x is the set of pairs (y, z) for which $(x, y, z) \in W$. By Theorem 2, §47,

$$(7) \qquad \xi(W_x) = \int_{A_x} f(x, y)\, d\mu_y.$$

Comparing (5), (6), and (7), we obtain

$$\int_A f(x, x)\, d\mu = \int_X \left(\int_{A_x} f(x, y)\, d\mu_y \right) d\mu_x.$$

This completes the proof of the theorem if $f(x, y) \geq 0$. The general case is reduced to the case $f(x, y) \geq 0$ by means of the relations

$$f(x, y) = f^+(x, y) - f^-(x, y),$$

$$f^+(x, y) = \tfrac{1}{2}[|f(x, y)| + f(x, y)], \qquad f^-(x, y) = \tfrac{1}{2}[|f(x, y)| - f(x, y)].$$

REMARK. It can be shown that if $f(x, y)$ is μ-measurable, then

$$\int_A f(x, y)\, d\mu$$

exists if

$$\int_X \left(\int_{A_x} |f(x, y)|\, d\mu_y \right) d\mu_x$$

exists.

EXAMPLES where (4) does not hold.

1. Let

$$A = [-1, 1]^2,$$
$$f(x, y) = xy/(x^2 + y^2)^2.$$

Then

$$\int_{-1}^{1} f(x, y) \, dx = 0 \qquad\qquad (y \neq 0),$$

and

$$\int_{-1}^{1} f(x, y) \, dy = 0 \qquad\qquad (x \neq 0).$$

Therefore

$$\int_{-1}^{1} \left(\int_{-1}^{1} f(x, y) \, dx \right) dy = \int_{-1}^{1} \left(\int_{-1}^{1} f(x, y) \, dy \right) dx = 0 ;$$

but the Lebesgue double integral over the square does not exist, since

$$\int_{-1}^{1} \int_{-1}^{1} |f(x, y)| \, dx \, dy \geq \int_{0}^{1} dr \int_{0}^{2\pi} (\sin \varphi \cos \varphi / r) \, d\varphi = 2 \int_{0}^{1} dr/r = \infty.$$

2. $A = [0, 1]^2$,

$$f(x, y) = \begin{cases} 2^{2n} & [(\tfrac{1}{2})^n \leq x < (\tfrac{1}{2})^{n-1}, \quad (\tfrac{1}{2})^n \leq y < (\tfrac{1}{2})^{n-1}], \\ -2^{2n+1} & [(\tfrac{1}{2})^{n+1} \leq x < (\tfrac{1}{2})^n, \quad (\tfrac{1}{2})^n \leq y < (\tfrac{1}{2})^{n-1}], \\ 0 & \text{(for all other points in the square).} \end{cases}$$

A simple calculation shows that

$$\int_{0}^{1} \left(\int_{0}^{1} f(x, y) \, dx \right) dy = 0, \qquad \int_{0}^{1} \left(\int_{0}^{1} f(x, y) \, dy \right) dx = 1.$$

EXERCISES

1. Suppose $f(x)$ and $g(y)$ are integrable over X and Y, respectively, and $h(x, y) = f(x)g(y)$. Show that $h(x, y)$ is ($\mu = \mu_x \otimes \mu_y$)-integrable over $X \times Y$ and

$$\int_{X \times Y} h(x, y) \, d\mu = \int_{X} f(x) \, d\mu_x \int_{Y} g(y) \, d\mu_y .$$

2. Suppose that $X = Y = [a, b]$ and that $\mu_x = \mu_y$ is linear Lebesgue measure. Let $f(x)$, $g(x)$ be integrable over X and periodic with period $b - a$. The *convolution* $f * g$ of f and g is also defined as a periodic function on $[a, b]$ by

$$(f * g)(x) = \int_{[a,b]} f(x - y)g(y) \, d\mu_y .$$

Show that $(f * g)(x)$ is integrable over X and

$$\int_X |(f*g)(x)|\, d\mu_x \leq \int_X |f(y)|\, d\mu_x \cdot \int_Y |g(y)|\, d\mu_y .$$

The integrability of $f * g$ demonstrates the existence of $(f * g)(x)$ for almost all $x \in X$. Hint: Use Fubini's theorem.

3. Suppose that $f(x)$ is integrable over $[0, b]$ with respect to Lebesgue measure. Suppose that $\alpha > 0$. The αth *fractional integral* of f is defined by

$$I_\alpha(f)(x) = [\Gamma(\alpha)]^{-1} \int_{[0,x]} (x - t)^{\alpha-1} f(t)\, d\mu_t$$

for $x \in [0, b]$, where $\Gamma(\alpha)$ is the Gamma function. Show that $I_\alpha(f)(x)$ is defined a.e. on $[0, b]$ and is integrable over $[0, a]$ for $a \in [0, b]$. Hint: Do directly as in Ex. 2, or use a suitable convolution of $f(x)$ with another function.

4. Suppose that $\alpha > 0$, $\beta > 0$, $f(x)$ is integrable on $[0, b]$ with respect to Lebesgue measure. By Ex. 3, $I_\beta[I_\alpha(f)(x)]$ is defined a.e. on $[0, b]$. Show that

$$I_\beta[I_\alpha(f)(x)] = I_{\alpha+\beta}(f)(x).$$

Hint: Use the result: for $p > 0$, $q > 0$,

$$\int_{[0,1]} x^{p-1}(1 - x)^{q-1}\, d\mu_x = \Gamma(p)\Gamma(q)/\Gamma(p + q).$$

5. (INTEGRATION BY PARTS.) Let $X = Y = [0, b]$ and let $\mu = \mu_x \otimes \mu_y$, where $\mu_x = \mu_y$ is linear Lebesgue measure.

Suppose that $f(x)$, $g(x)$ are integrable over X. If

$$F(x) = \int_{[0,x]} f(x)\, d\mu_x, \qquad G(x) = \int_{[0,x]} g(x)\, d\mu_x$$

for $x \in [0, 1]$, then

$$\int_X F(x)g(x)\, d\mu_x = F(b)G(b) - \int_X f(x)G(x)\, d\mu_x .$$

The result may be demonstrated as follows:

a) Let $E = \{(x, y) : (x, y) \in X \times Y, y \leq x\}$. Show that E is μ-measurable. Hence χ_E is μ-measurable and $H(x, y) = \chi_E(x, y)g(x)f(y)$ is also μ-measurable.

b) Show that $H(x, y)$ is integrable over $X \times Y$ with respect to μ. (Apply Ex. 1.)

c) Apply Fubini's theorem to obtain

$$\int_X F(x)g(x)\,d\mu_x = \int_{X \times Y} H(x,\,y)\,d\mu = \int_Y f(y)\left(\int_{[y,b]} g(x)\,d\mu_x\right)d\mu_y.$$

This will yield the stated result.

§49. The integral as a set function

We shall consider the integral $F(A) = \int_A f(x)\,d\mu$ as a set function on the assumption that $S\mu$ is a Borel algebra with unit X and that $\int_X f(x)\,d\mu$ exists.

Then, as we have already proved:

1. $F(A)$ is defined on the Borel algebra S_μ.
2. $F(A)$ is real-valued.
3. $F(A)$ is additive, that is, if

$$A = \bigcup_n A_n \qquad\qquad (A,\,A_n \in S_\mu),$$

then

$$F(A) = \sum_n F(A_n).$$

4. $F(A)$ is absolutely continuous, that is, $\mu(A) = 0$ implies that

$$F(A) = 0.$$

We state the following important theorem without proof:

RADON'S THEOREM. *If a set function $F(A)$ has properties 1, 2, 3 and 4, it is representable in the form*

$$F(A) = \int_A f(x)\,d\mu.$$

We shall show that the function $f = dF/d\mu$ is uniquely defined a.e. In fact, if

$$F(A) = \int_A f_1(x)\,d\mu = \int_A f_2(x)\,d\mu$$

for all $A \in S_\mu$, then

$$\mu(A_n) \leq n \int_{A_n} (f_1 - f_2)\,d\mu = 0$$

for arbitrary n, where

$$A_n = \{x : f_1(x) - f_2(x) > 1/n\}.$$

Similarly,

$$\mu(B_n) = 0$$

for

$$B_n = \{x : f_2(x) - f_1(x) > 1/n\}.$$

Since

$$\{x : f_1(x) \neq f_2(x)\} = \mathsf{U}_n A_n \cup \mathsf{U}_m B_m,$$

it follows that

$$\mu\{x : f_1(x) \neq f_2(x)\} = 0.$$

This proves our assertion.

EXERCISES

1. With the notation of this section, suppose that $f(x) \geq 0$ and let $\nu(A) = \int_A f(x)\, d\mu$. Then the conditions listed before Radon's theorem can be paraphrased by saying that $\nu(A)$ is a completely additive, absolutely continuous measure on the Borel algebra S_μ. Show that if $g(x)$ is integrable over X with respect to ν, then

$$\int_A g(x)\, d\nu = \int_A f(x)g(x)\, d\mu \qquad\qquad (A \in S_\mu).$$

2. If $\nu(A)$ is a completely additive measure on the Borel algebra S_μ, then ν may have the following property: For $\epsilon > 0$ there exists a $\delta > 0$ such that $A \in S_\mu$ and $\mu(A) < \delta$ imply $\nu(A) < \epsilon$. It is easy to see that if ν has this property, then ν is absolutely continuous with respect to μ, i.e., $\mu(A) = 0$ implies $\nu(A) = 0$. Show, conversely, that if ν is absolutely continuous with respect to μ, then ν has the above (ϵ, δ) property.

Chapter VIII

SQUARE INTEGRABLE FUNCTIONS

One of the most important linear normed spaces in Functional Analysis is Hilbert space, named after the German mathematician David Hilbert, who introduced this space in his research on the theory of integral equations. It is the natural infinite-dimensional analogue of Euclidean n-space. We became acquainted with one of the important realizations of Hilbert space in Chapter III—the space l_2, whose elements are the sequences

$$x = (x_1, \cdots, x_n, \cdots)$$

satisfying the condition

$$\sum_{n=1}^{\infty} x_n^2 < \infty.$$

We can now use the Lebesgue integral to introduce a second, in certain respects more convenient, realization of Hilbert space—the space of square integrable functions. In this chapter we consider the definition and fundamental properties of the space of square integrable functions and show that it is isometric (if certain assumptions are made about the measure used in the integral) to the space l_2.

We shall give an axiomatic definition of Hilbert space in Chapter IX.

§50. The space L_2

In the sequel we consider functions $f(x)$ defined on a set R, on which a measure $\mu(E)$ is prescribed, satisfying the condition $\mu(R) < \infty$. The functions $f(x)$ are assumed to be measurable and defined a.e. on R. We shall not distinguish between functions equivalent on R. For brevity, instead of $\int_R$ we write simply $\int$.

DEFINITION 1. We say that $f(x)$ is a *square integrable* (or *summable*) *function* on R if the integral

$$\int f^2(x)\, d\mu$$

exists (is finite). The collection of all square integrable functions is denoted by L_2.

The fundamental properties of such functions follow.

THEOREM 1. *The product of two square integrable functions is an integrable function.*

The proof follows immediately from the inequality

$$| f(x)g(x) | \leq \tfrac{1}{2}[f^2(x) + g^2(x)]$$

and the properties of the Lebesgue integral.

COROLLARY 1. *A square integrable function* $f(x)$ *is integrable.*

For, it is sufficient to set $g(x) \equiv 1$ in Theorem 1.

THEOREM 2. *The sum of two functions of* L_2 *is an element of* L_2.

Proof. Indeed,

$$[f(x) + g(x)]^2 \leq f^2(x) + 2 \,| f(x)g(x) | + g^2(x),$$

and Theorem 1 implies that the three functions on the right are summable.

THEOREM 3. *If* $f(x) \in L_2$ *and* α *is an arbitrary number, then* $\alpha f(x) \in L_2$.

Proof. If $f \in L_2$, then

$$\int [\alpha f(x)]^2 \, d\mu = \alpha^2 \int f^2(x) \, d\mu < \infty.$$

Theorems 2 and 3 show that a linear combination of functions of L_2 is an element of L_2; it is also obvious that the addition of functions and multiplication of functions by numbers satisfy the eight conditions of the definition of a linear space (Chapter III, §21). Hence L_2 is a linear space.

We now define an *inner* (or a *scalar*) product in L_2 by setting

(1)
$$(f, g) = \int_R f(x)g(x) \, d\mu.$$

An inner product is a real-valued function of pairs of vectors of a linear space satisfying the following conditions:

1) $(f, g) = (g, f)$.
2) $(f_1 + f_2, g) = (f_1, g) + (f_2, g)$.
3) $(\lambda f, g) = \lambda(f, g)$.
4) $(f, f) > 0$ if $f \neq 0$.

The fundamental properties of the integral immediately imply that Conditions 1)–3) are satisfied by (1). Inasmuch as we have agreed not to distinguish between equivalent functions (so that, in particular, the null element in L_2 is the collection of all functions on R equivalent to $f \equiv 0$), Condition 4) is also satisfied (see the Corollary to Theorem 9, §43). We therefore arrive at the following

DEFINITION 2. The space L_2 is the Euclidean space (a linear space with an inner product) whose elements are the classes of equivalent square integrable functions; addition of the elements of L_2 and multiplication by scalars are defined in the way usual for functions and the inner product is defined by

(1) $$(f, g) = \int f(x)g(x)\, d\mu.$$

The Schwarz inequality, which in this case has the form

(2) $$\left(\int f(x)g(x)\, d\mu\right)^2 \le \int f^2(x)\, d\mu \cdot \int g^2(x)\, d\mu,$$

is satisfied in L_2, as it is in every Euclidean space (see Ex. 3, §56). The same is true for the triangle inequality

(3) $$\left\{\int [f(x) + g(x)]^2\, d\mu\right\}^{\frac{1}{2}} \le \left\{\int f^2(x)\, d\mu\right\}^{\frac{1}{2}} + \left\{\int g^2(x)\, d\mu\right\}^{\frac{1}{2}}.$$

In particular, the Schwarz inequality yields the following useful inequality:

(4) $$\left(\int f(x)\, d\mu\right)^2 \le \mu(R) \int f^2(x)\, d\mu.$$

To introduce a norm into L_2 we set

(5) $$\| f \| = (f, f)^{\frac{1}{2}} = \left[\int f^2(x)\, d\mu\right]^{\frac{1}{2}} \qquad (f \in L_2).$$

EXERCISE. Using the properties 1)–4) of the inner product, prove that the norm defined by (5) satisfies Conditions 1–3 of the definition of a norm in §21.

The following theorem plays an important part in many problems of analysis:

THEOREM 4. *The space L_2 is complete.*

Proof. a) Let $\{f_n(x)\}$ be a fundamental sequence in L_2, i.e.,

$$\| f_n - f_m \| \to 0 \qquad (n, m \to \infty).$$

Then there is a subsequence of indices $\{n_k\}$ such that

$$\| f_{n_k} - f_{n_{k+1}} \| \le (\tfrac{1}{2})^k.$$

Hence, in view of inequality (4), it follows that

$$\int | f_{n_k}(x) - f_{n_{k+1}}(x) |\, d\mu \le [\mu(R)]^{\frac{1}{2}} \left\{\int [f_{n_k}(x) - f_{n_{k+1}}(x)]^2\, d\mu\right\}^{\frac{1}{2}}$$

$$\le (\tfrac{1}{2})^k [\mu(R)]^{\frac{1}{2}}.$$

This inequality and the Corollary to Theorem 2, §44 imply that the series

$$| f_{n_1}(x) | + | f_{n_2}(x) - f_{n_1}(x) | + \cdots$$

converges a.e. on R. Then the series

$$f_{n_1}(x) + [f_{n_2}(x) - f_{n_1}(x)] + \cdots$$

also converges a.e. on R to a function

(6) $f(x) = \lim_{k \to \infty} f_{n_k}(x).$

Hence, we have proved that if $\{f_n(x)\}$ is a fundamental sequence of functions in L_2, it contains an a.e. convergent subsequence.

b) We shall now show that the function $f(x)$ defined by (6) is an element of L_2 and that

(7) $\| f_n(x) - f(x) \| \to 0$ $(n \to \infty).$

For sufficiently large k and l,

$$\int [f_{n_k}(x) - f_{n_l}(x)]^2 \, d\mu < \epsilon.$$

In view of Theorem 3, §44, we may take the limit under the integral sign in this inequality as $l \to \infty$. We obtain

$$\int [f_{n_k}(x) - f(x)]^2 \, d\mu \leq \epsilon.$$

It follows that $f \in L_2$ and $f_{n_k} \to f$. But the convergence of a subsequence of a fundamental sequence to a limit implies that the sequence itself converges to the same limit. [Convergence here means the fulfillment of (7); in this connection see §51.] This proves the theorem.

EXERCISES

1. If we define the distance $d(f_1, f_2)$ in $L_2(R, \mu)$ as

$$d(f_1, f_2) = \| f_1 - f_2 \| = \{ \int [f_1(x) - f_2(x)]^2 \, dx \}^{\frac{1}{2}},$$

then d satisfies the axioms for a metric space (see vol. 1, §8). Furthermore, d is translation invariant, i.e.,

$$d(f_1 + f, f_2 + f) = d(f_1, f_2)$$

for $f_1, f_2, f \in L_2$. This result, of course, holds in any normed linear space (see vol. 1, §21).

2. Let $R = [0, 1]$ and let μ be linear Lebesgue measure. Show that $\{f : \| f \| \leq 1\}$ is closed and bounded, but not compact.

3. With the notation of Ex. 2, show that the set of continuous functions on $[0, 1]$ is a linear manifold in L_2, but is not a subspace, i.e., is not closed. (For the terminology, see §57.)

4. A measurable function $f(x)$ is said to be *essentially bounded* (on R) if there exists an $a > 0$ such that $|f(x)| \leq a$ a.e. on R. The number a is called an *essential upper bound* of f on R. For an essentially bounded function f, let $m = \inf \{a : a$ an essential upper bound of $f\}$. The number m is called the essential supremum of f: $m = \text{ess. sup } f$.

a) Show that ess. sup f is the smallest essential upper bound of f on R.

b) Let $L_\infty(R, \mu)$ be the collection of essentially bounded functions on R. If we put $\| f \| = \text{ess. sup } f$, show that L_∞ becomes a normed linear space.

5. Let $L_p(R, \mu)$, $p \geq 1$, be the set of measurable functions f defined on R for which $|f(x)|^p$ is integrable over R.

a) If a, b are real numbers, show that

$$|a + b|^p \leq 2^p(|a|^p + |b|^p).$$

(The condition $p \geq 1$ is essential here.)

b) Show then that $L_p(R, \mu)$ is a linear space, i.e., $f, g \in L_p$ implies that $f + g \in L_p$ and that $f \in L_p$ and a real imply $af \in L_p$. Define $\| f \|_p = \left[\int_R |f(x)|^p \, d\mu \right]^{1/p}$. We shall shortly see that L_p is a normed space with $\| f \|_p$ as norm.

6. a) Suppose $p > 1$. Define q by the equation $1/p + 1/q = 1$. p and q are called *conjugate exponents*. Let $v = f(u) = u^{p-1}$. Then $u = g(v) = v^{1/p-1}$. Verify that the hypotheses of Young's inequality (§47, Ex. 5) are satisfied and that $F(u) = u^p/p$, $G(v) = v^q/q$, and that therefore

$$uv \leq u^p/p + v^q/q,$$

with equality if, and only if, $u^p = v^q$.

b) (HÖLDER INEQUALITY.) Suppose $f \in L_p(R, \mu)$, $g \in L_q(R, \mu)$, with p, q conjugate exponents. Show that

$$f(x)g(x) \in L_1(R, \mu) = L$$

and

$$\left| \int_R f(x)g(x) \, d\mu \right| \leq \int_R |f(x)g(x)| \, d\mu$$

$$\leq \left(\int_R |f(x)|^p \, d\mu \right)^{1/p} \left(\int_R |g(x)|^q \, d\mu \right)^{1/q}$$

$$= \| f \|_p \| g \|_q.$$

This result may be obtained as follows: It is trivial if $\| f \|_p = 0$ or $\| g \|_q = 0$. Otherwise, put

$$u = |f(x)| / \|f\|_p, \qquad v = |g(x)| / \|g\|_q$$

in the result of a), and integrate over R (see vol. 1, p. 20).

c) (MINKOWSKI'S INEQUALITY.) If $f, g \in L_p(R, \mu)$, then

$$\|f + g\|_p \leq \|f\|_p + \|g\|_p,$$

or, in terms of integrals,

$$\left(\int_R |f(x) + g(x)|^p \, d\mu \right)^{1/p} \leq \left(\int_R |f(x)|^p \, d\mu \right)^{1/p} + \left(\int_R |g(x)|^p \, d\mu \right)^{1/p}.$$

If $\|f + g\|_p = 0$, then the result is clear. If $\|f + g\|_p > 0$, observe that

$$|f(x) + g(x)|^p \leq |f(x)| \, |f(x) + g(x)|^{p-1} + |g(x)| \, |f(x) + g(x)|^{p-1},$$

$$|f(x) + g(x)|^{p-1} \in L_q.$$

Apply Hölder's inequality to each term on the right to obtain

$$\int_R |f + g|^p \, d\mu \leq \left(\int_R |f + g|^p \, d\mu \right)^{1/q} (\|f\|_p + \|g\|_p).$$

It is now clear that $L_p(R, \mu)$ with norm $\|f\|_p$ is a normed linear space for $p > 1$. Note also that if $p = 2$, then $q = 2$, and Hölder's inequality reduces to the Schwarz inequality.

§51. Mean convergence. Dense subsets of L_2

The introduction of a norm in L_2 determines a new notion of convergence for square integrable functions:

$$f_n \to f \qquad \qquad \text{(in } L_2)$$

if

$$\lim_{n \to \infty} \int [f_n(x) - f(x)]^2 \, d\mu = 0.$$

This type of convergence of functions is called *mean convergence*, or, more precisely, mean square convergence.

Let us consider the relation of mean convergence to uniform convergence and convergence a.e. (see Chapter VI).

THEOREM 1. *If a sequence $\{f_n(x)\}$ of functions of L_2 converges uniformly to $f(x)$, then $f(x) \in L_2$, and $\{f_n(x)\}$ is mean convergent to $f(x)$.*

Proof. Suppose that $\epsilon > 0$. If n is sufficiently large,

$$|f_n(x) - f(x)| < \epsilon,$$

whence

$$\int [f_n(x) - f(x)]^2 \, d\mu < \epsilon^2 \mu(R).$$

The theorem follows at once from this inequality.

Theorem 1 implies that if an arbitrary $f \in L_2$ can be approximated with arbitrary accuracy by functions $f_n \in M \subseteq L_2$ in the sense of uniform convergence, then it can be approximated by such functions in the sense of mean convergence.

Hence an arbitrary function $f \in L_2$ can be approximated with arbitrary accuracy by *simple* functions belonging to L_2.

We prove that an arbitrary simple function $f \in L_2$, and consequently an arbitrary function of L_2, can be approximated to any desired degree of accuracy by simple functions whose set of distinct values is finite.

Suppose that $f(x)$ assumes the values $y_1, \cdots, y_n, \cdots$ on the sets $E_1, \cdots, E_n, \cdots$. Inasmuch as f^2 is summable, the series

$$\sum_n y_n^2 \mu(E_n) = \int f^2(x) \, d\mu$$

converges. Choose an N such that

$$\sum_{n>N} y_n^2 \mu(E_n) < \epsilon,$$

and set

$$f_N(x) = \begin{cases} f(x) & (x \in E_i, i \leq N), \\ 0 & (x \in E_i, i > N). \end{cases}$$

Then

$$\int [f(x) - f_N(x)]^2 \, d\mu = \sum_{n>N} y_n^2 \mu(E_n) < \epsilon,$$

that is, the function $f_N(x)$, which assumes a finite set of values, approximates the function f with arbitrary accuracy.

Let R be a metric space with a measure possessing the following property (which is satisfied in all cases of practical interest): all the open and closed sets of R are measurable, and

$(*)$ $\mu^*(M) = \inf \{\mu(G); M \subseteq G\}$

for all $M \subseteq R$, where the lower bound is taken over all open sets G containing M. Then we have

THEOREM 2. *The set of all continuous functions on R is dense in L_2.*

Proof. In view of the preceding discussion, it is sufficient to prove that every simple function assuming a finite number of values is the limit, in the sense of mean convergence, of continuous functions. Furthermore, since every simple function assuming a finite set of values is a linear combination of characteristic functions $\chi_M(x)$ of measurable sets, it is enough to carry out the proof for such functions. Let M be a measurable set in the metric space R. Then it follows at once from the Condition (∗) that for every $\epsilon > 0$ there exists a closed set F_M and an open set G_M such that

$$F_M \subseteq M \subseteq G_M, \qquad \mu(G_M) - \mu(F_M) < \epsilon.$$

We now define

$$\varphi_\epsilon(x) = \rho(x, R \setminus G_M)/[\rho(x, R \setminus G_M) + \rho(x, F_M)].$$

This function is 0 on $R \setminus G_M$ and 1 on F_M. It is continuous, since $\rho(x, F_M)$, $\rho(x, R \setminus G_M)$ are continuous and their sum does not vanish. The function $\chi_M(x) - \varphi_\epsilon(x)$ is bounded by 1 on $G_M \setminus F_M$ and vanishes in the complement of this set. Consequently,

$$\int [\chi_M(x) - \varphi_\epsilon(x)]^2 \, d\mu < \epsilon,$$

and the theorem follows.

THEOREM 3. *If a sequence $\{f_n(x)\}$ converges to $f(x)$ in the mean, it contains a subsequence $\{f_{n_k}(x)\}$ which converges to $f(x)$ a.e.*

Proof. If $\{f_n(x)\}$ converges in the mean, it is a fundamental sequence in L_2. Therefore, repeating the reasoning in Part a) of the proof of Theorem 4, §50, we obtain a subsequence $\{f_{n_k}(x)\}$ of $\{f_n(x)\}$ which converges a.e. to a function $\varphi(x)$. Furthermore, Part b) of the same proof shows that $\{f_{n_k}(x)\}$ converges to $\varphi(x)$ in the mean. Hence, $\varphi(x) = f(x)$ a.e.

★ It is not hard to find examples to show that convergence in the mean does not imply convergence a.e. In fact, the sequence of functions $\{f_{n_k}\}$ defined on p. 45 obviously converges in the mean to $f \equiv 0$, but (as was shown) does not converge a.e. We shall now show that convergence a.e. (and even everywhere) does not imply mean convergence. Let

$$f_n(x) = \begin{cases} n & [x \in (0, 1/n)], \\ 0 & \text{for all remaining values of } x. \end{cases}$$

It is clear that the sequence $\{f_n(x)\}$ converges to 0 everywhere on $[0, 1]$, but that

$$\int_0^1 f_n^2(x) \, dx = n \to \infty.$$

The Chebyshev inequality (§43, Theorem 9) implies that if a sequence is mean convergent, it converges in measure. Therefore, Theorem 3, which we have proved in this section independently of the Chebyshev inequality, follows from Theorem 4, §41. The relations between the various types of convergence of functions can be schematized as follows:

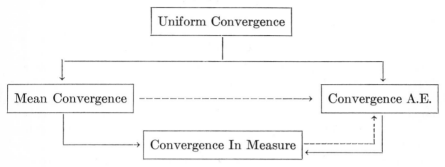

where the dotted arrows mean that a sequence converging in measure contains a subsequence converging a.e. and that a sequence converging in the mean contains a subsequence converging a.e. ★

EXERCISES

1. If $\{f_n(x)\}$ converges to $f(x)$ in the mean and $\{f_n(x)\}$ converges pointwise a.e. to $g(x)$, then $f(x) = g(x)$ a.e. on R.

2. a) If $\{f_n(x)\} \subset L_2$, $\{f_n(x)\}$ converges to $f(x)$ pointwise a.e. and $|f_n(x)| \leq g(x)$, $g \in L_2$, then $\{f_n(x)\}$ converges in the mean to $f(x)$, i.e., $\|f_n - f\|_2 \to 0$.

   b) The corresponding result obtains for L_p $(p > 1)$.

3. a) If $\|f_n - f\|_2 \to 0$, then $\|f_n\|_2 \to \|f\|_2$; hence

$$\lim_{n \to \infty} \int_R |f_n(x)|^2 \, d\mu = \int_R |f(x)|^2 \, d\mu.$$

   b) The corresponding result obtains for L_p $(p > 1)$.

4. a) Let $\{f_n(x)\}$ converge to $f(x)$ in the mean and suppose $g(x) \in L_2$. Then $\{f_n(x)g(x)\}$ converges to $f(x)g(x)$.

   b) More generally, if $\|f_n - f\|_2 \to 0$ and $\|g_n - g\|_2 \to 0$, then $\|f_n g_n - fg\|_2 \to 0$.

   c) Similar results obtain for $f_n, f \in L^p$; $g_n, g \in L^q$, with $1/p + 1/q = 1$, $p > 1$.

   d) Let $R = [a, b]$, and let μ be linear Lebesgue measure. Then $\{f_n\}$ converges to f in the mean implies that

$$\lim_{n \to \infty} \int_{[a, x_0]} f_n(x) \, d\mu = \int_{[a, x_0]} f(x) \, d\mu \qquad (a \leq x_0 \leq b).$$

Hint: Choose

$$g(x) = \begin{cases} 1 & (a \leq x < x_0), \\ 0 & (x > x_0). \end{cases}$$

Show that $g \in L_2$.

§52. L_2 spaces with countable bases

The space L_2 of square integrable functions depends, in general, on the choice of the space R and the measure μ. To designate it fully it should be written as $L_2(R, \mu)$. The space $L_2(R, \mu)$ is finite-dimensional only in exceptional cases. The spaces $L_2(R, \mu)$ which are most important for analysis are the spaces which have *infinite dimension* (this term will be explained below).

To characterize these spaces, we need an additional concept from the theory of measure.

We can introduce a metric in the collection $\mathfrak{M}$ of measurable subsets of the space R (whose measure we have assumed to be finite) by setting

$$\rho(A, B) = \mu(A \; \Delta \; B).$$

If we identify sets A and B for which $\mu(A \; \Delta \; B) = 0$ (that is, we consider sets which are the same except for a set of measure zero to be indistinguishable), then the set $\mathfrak{M}$ together with the metric ρ becomes a metric space.

DEFINITION. A measure μ is said to have a *countable base* if the metric space $\mathfrak{M}$ contains a countable dense set.

In other words, a measure μ has a countable base if there is a countable set

$$\mathfrak{D} = \{A_n\} \qquad\qquad (n = 1, 2, \cdots)$$

of measurable subsets of R (a countable base for the measure μ) such that for every measurable $M \subseteq R$ and $\epsilon > 0$ there is an $A_k \in \mathfrak{D}$ for which

$$\mu(M \; \Delta \; A_k) < \epsilon.$$

In particular, a measure μ obviously has a countable base if it is the extension of a measure defined on a countable collection S_m of sets. Indeed, in that case the ring $\mathfrak{R}(S_m)$ (which is obviously countable) is the required base, in view of Theorem 3, §38.

In particular, Lebesgue measure on a closed interval of the real line is induced by the set of intervals with rational endpoints as elementary sets. Since the collection of all such intervals is countable, Lebesgue measure has a countable base.

The product $\mu = \mu_1 \otimes \mu_2$ of two measures with countable bases also has a countable base, since, as is easily seen, the finite unions of the products of pairs of elements of the bases of μ_1 and μ_2 form a base for $\mu = \mu_1 \otimes \mu_2$. Therefore, Lebesgue measure in the plane (as well as in n-dimensional space) has a countable base.

Suppose that

(1) $$A_1^*, \cdots, A_n^*, \cdots$$

is a countable base for μ. It is easy to see that the base (1) can be extended to a base

(2) $$A_1, \cdots, A_n, \cdots$$

of μ with the following properties:

1) The base (2) is closed under differences.
2) R is an element of the base (2).

Conditions 1) and 2) imply that (2) is closed under finite unions and intersections. This follows from the following relations:

$$A_1 \cap A_2 = A_1 \setminus (A_1 \setminus A_2),$$
$$A_1 \cup A_2 = R \setminus [(R \setminus A_1) \cap (R \setminus A_2)].$$

THEOREM. *If a measure μ has a countable base, then $L_2(R, \mu)$ contains a countable dense set.*

Proof. The finite sums

(3) $$\sum_{k=1}^n c_k f_k(x),$$

where the c_k are rational numbers and the $f_k(x)$ are characteristic functions of the elements of the countable base of μ, form the required base for $L_2(R, \mu)$.

For, as we have already shown in the preceding section, the set of simple functions assuming only a finite number of values, is everywhere dense in L_2. Since it is obvious that an arbitrary function of this set can be approximated with arbitrary accuracy by functions of the same form, but assuming only rational values, and since the set of functions of the form (3) is countable, to prove the theorem it is sufficient to show that an arbitrary simple function $f(x)$, assuming the values

$$y_1, \cdots, y_n \qquad (y_i \text{ rational})$$

on the sets

$$E_1, \cdots, E_n \qquad [\textstyle\bigcup_i E_i = R, \; E_i \cap E_j = \emptyset \; (i \neq j)],$$

can be approximated with arbitrary accuracy by functions of the form (3) in the sense of the metric in L_2. In view of this remark, we may assume without loss of generality that the base for μ satisfies 1) and 2).

By definition, for every $\epsilon > 0$ there exist sets $A_1, \cdots, A_n$ of the base for μ such that $\rho(E_k, A_k) < \epsilon$, that is,

$$\mu[(E_k \setminus A_k) \cup (A_k \setminus E_k)] < \epsilon.$$

We set

$$A_1' = A_1,$$
$$A_k' = A_k \setminus \bigcup_{i<k} A_i \qquad (2 \leq k \leq n),$$

and define

$$f^*(x) = \begin{cases} y_k & (x \in A_k'), \\ 0 & (x \in R \setminus \bigcup_{i=1}^n A_i'). \end{cases}$$

It is easy to see that

$$\mu\{x : f(x) \neq f^*(x)\}$$

is arbitrarily small for sufficiently small ϵ, and that consequently the integral

$$\int [f(x) - f^*(x)]^2 \, d\mu \leq (2 \max |y_n|)^2 \, \mu\{x : f(x) \neq f^*(x)\}$$

is arbitrarily small for sufficiently small ϵ.

In view of our assumptions about the base of μ, $f^*(x)$ is of the form (3). This proves the theorem.

If R is a closed interval on the real line and μ is Lebesgue measure, a countable base in $L_2(R, \mu)$ can be obtained in a more classical way: for instance, the set of all polynomials with rational coefficients forms a base in L_2. This set is dense (even in the sense of uniform convergence) in the set of continuous functions, and the latter are a dense set in $L_2(R, \mu)$.

In the sequel we restrict ourselves to spaces $L_2(R, \mu)$ with countable dense subsets [that is, separable spaces (see §9)].

EXERCISES

1. Let X be the unit square in the plane, μ the σ-additive measure that is the Lebesgue extension of the measure defined in §35, Ex. 2 (see also §37, Ex. 3). Note that to obtain the Lebesgue extension we must use the method of §39 since the semi-ring of horizontal cells has no unit.

Show that μ is not separable.

Hint: Any $A \in S_\mu$ is a countable union of horizontal line segments; hence, any countable collection of elements of S_μ contains a countable set of horizontal line segments $\{A_n\}$. We can choose $y_0 \in [0, 1]$ such that

$$A_0 = \{(x, y) : 0 \le x \le 1, y = y_0\}$$

is disjoint from all these. Then show that

$$\rho(A_0, A_n) = \mu(A_0 \triangle A_n) \ge 1$$

for all n.

2. a) Since $\mu(R) < \infty$, a simple measurable function with only finitely many distinct values belongs to $L_p(R, \mu)$ for every $p \ge 1$.

b) The discussion in §51 can be paralleled for the present case to show that every $f \in L_p$ can be approximated in the mean of order p (i.e., in the metric of L_p) by simple functions assuming only finitely many values.

c) The procedure of §52 can now be imitated to show that if μ has a countable base, then $L_p(R, \mu)$ is separable for $p \ge 1$.

d) It follows from a) and c) that for $r, s \ge 1$, $L_r(R, \mu)$ is dense in $L_s(R, \mu)$.

§53. Orthogonal sets of functions. Orthogonalization

In this section we consider functions $f \in L_2$ defined on a measurable set R with measure μ, which we assume to have a countable base and to satisfy the condition $\mu(R) < \infty$. As before, we do not distinguish between equivalent functions.

DEFINITION 1. A set of functions

$$(1) \qquad\qquad \varphi_1(x), \, \cdots, \, \varphi_n(x)$$

is said to be *linearly dependent* if there exist constants $c_1, \, \cdots, \, c_n$, not all zero, such that

$$(2) \qquad\qquad c_1\varphi_1(x) + c_2\varphi_2(x) + \cdots + c_n\varphi_n(x) = 0$$

a.e. on R. If, however, (2) implies that

$$(3) \qquad\qquad c_1 = \cdots = c_n = 0,$$

then the set (1) is said to be *linearly independent*.

Clearly, a linearly independent set cannot contain functions equivalent to $\psi(x) \equiv 0$.

DEFINITION 2. An infinite sequence of functions

$$(4) \qquad\qquad \varphi_1(x), \, \cdots, \, \varphi_n(x), \, \cdots$$

is said to be linearly independent if every finite subset of (4) is linearly independent.

We denote by

$$M = M(\varphi_1, \, \cdots, \, \varphi_n, \, \cdots) = M\{\varphi_k\}$$

the set of all finite linear combinations of functions of (4). This set is called the *linear hull* of (4) (or the *linear manifold generated by* $\{\varphi_k\}$). We let

$$\bar{M} = \bar{M}(\varphi_1, \cdots, \varphi_n, \cdots) = \bar{M}\{\varphi_k\}$$

denote the closure of M in L_2. $\bar{M}$ is called the *closed linear hull* of (4) (or the *subspace generated by* $\{\varphi_k\}$).

It is easily seen that $\bar{M}$ consists precisely of the functions $f \in L_2$ which can be approximated by finite linear combinations of functions of (4) with arbitrarily prescribed accuracy.

DEFINITION 3. The set of functions (4) is said to be *complete* (sometimes *closed*) if

$$\bar{M} = L_2.$$

Suppose that L_2 contains a countable dense set of functions

$$f_1, \cdots, f_n, \cdots.$$

Deleting from this set those functions which are linearly dependent on the preceding functions in the sequence, we obtain a linearly independent set of functions

$$g_1, \cdots, g_n, \cdots$$

which, as is easily seen, is complete.

If L_2 contains a finite complete set (1) of linearly independent functions, then

$$L_2 = \bar{M}(\varphi_1, \cdots, \varphi_n) = M(\varphi_1, \cdots, \varphi_n)$$

is isomorphic to Euclidean n-space. We say L_2 is n-dimensional. Otherwise, we call L_2 infinite-dimensional.

The space L_2 is infinite-dimensional in all cases of interest in analysis.

Obviously, in order that (4) be complete it is sufficient that it be possible to approximate every function of a dense subset of L_2 with arbitrary accuracy by linear combinations of functions of (4).

Let $R = [a, b]$ be a closed interval on the real line with the usual Lebesgue measure. Then the set of functions

(5) $$1, x, x^2, \cdots, x^n, \cdots$$

is complete in $L_2(R, \mu)$.

For, according to the Weierstrass theorem (see Vol. 1, p. 25) the set of linear combinations of functions (5) is dense in the set of all continuous functions. The completeness of the set (5) now follows from this remark and Theorem 2, §51.

Two functions $f(x)$ and $g(x)$ of L_2 are said to be *orthogonal* if

$$(f, g) = \int f(x)g(x) \, d\mu = 0.$$

We shall call every set of functions $\varphi_1, \cdots, \varphi_n, \cdots$, which are distinct from zero and are pairwise orthogonal, an *orthogonal set*. An orthogonal set is said to be *normalized* or *orthonormal* if $\| \varphi_n \| = 1$ for all n; in other words,

$$\varphi_1, \cdots, \varphi_n, \cdots$$

is an orthonormal set of functions if

$$(\varphi_i, \varphi_k) = \int \varphi_i(x)\varphi_k(x) \, d\mu = \begin{cases} 0 & (i \neq k), \\ 1 & (i = k). \end{cases}$$

EXAMPLES: 1. A classical example of an orthonormal set of functions on the closed interval $[-\pi, \pi]$ is the set of trigonometric functions

$$(2\pi)^{-\frac{1}{2}}, (\pi)^{-\frac{1}{2}} \cos x, (\pi)^{-\frac{1}{2}} \cos 2x, \cdots, (\pi)^{-\frac{1}{2}} \sin x, (\pi)^{-\frac{1}{2}} \sin 2x, \cdots.$$

2. The polynomials

$$P_n(x) = (2^n n!)^{-1} (d^n[(x^2 - 1)^n]/dx^n) \qquad (n = 0, 1, 2, \cdots),$$

called the *Legendre polynomials*, form an orthogonal set of functions on $[-1, 1]$. An orthonormal set consists of the functions

$$[\tfrac{1}{2}(2n + 1)]^{\frac{1}{2}} P_n(x).$$

It is easily seen that *an orthonormal set of functions is linearly independent*. For, multiplying the relation

$$c_1 \varphi_1 + \cdots + c_n \varphi_n = 0$$

by φ_i and integrating, we obtain

$$c_i(\varphi_i, \varphi_i) = 0,$$

and since $(\varphi_i, \varphi_i) > 0$, $c_i = 0$.

We note further, that *if the space L_2 contains a countable dense set $f_1, \cdots, f_n, \cdots$, then an arbitrary orthonormal set of functions $\{\varphi_\alpha\}$ is at most countable*.

To see this, suppose that $\alpha \neq \beta$. Then

$$\| \varphi_\alpha - \varphi_\beta \| = 2^{\frac{1}{2}}.$$

For every α choose an f_α from the dense subset such that

$$\| \varphi_\alpha - f_\alpha \| < 2^{-\frac{1}{2}}.$$

Clearly, $f_\alpha \neq f_\beta$ if $\alpha \neq \beta$. Since the set of all f_α is countable, the set of φ_α is at most countable.

An orthonormal base is of great importance in studying finite-dimensional spaces. In this connection an orthonormal base is a set of orthogonal unit vectors, whose linear hull coincides with the whole space. In the infinite-dimensional case the analogue of such a base is a complete orthonormal set of functions, that is, a set

$$\varphi_1 , \cdots , \varphi_n , \cdots$$

such that

  1) $(\varphi_i , \varphi_k) = \delta_{ik}$,
  2) $\bar{M}(\varphi_1 , \cdots , \varphi_n , \cdots) = L_2$.

We gave examples of orthonormal sets of functions on the intervals $[-\pi, \pi]$ and $[-1, 1]$ above. The existence of a complete orthonormal set of functions in an arbitrary separable space L_2 is a consequence of the following theorem:

THEOREM. *Suppose that the set of functions*

(6) $$f_1 , \cdots , f_n , \cdots$$

is linearly independent. Then there exists a set of functions

(7) $$\varphi_1 , \cdots , \varphi_n , \cdots$$

satisfying the following conditions:

  1) *The set* (7) *is orthonormal.*
  2) *Every function* φ_n *is a linear combination of the functions* $f_1 , \cdots , f_n$:

$$\varphi_n = a_{n1}f_1 + a_{n2}f_2 + \cdots + a_{nn}f_n ,$$

with $a_{nn} \neq 0$.

  3) *Every function* f_n *is a linear combination of the functions*

$$f_n = b_{n1}\varphi_1 + \cdots + b_{nn}\varphi_n ,$$

with $b_{nn} \neq 0$.

Every function of the set (7) *is uniquely determined (except for sign) by the Conditions* 1)–3).

Proof. The function $\varphi_1(x)$ is uniquely determined (except for sign) by the conditions of the theorem. For,

$$\varphi_1 = a_{11}f_1 ,$$

$$(\varphi_1 , \varphi_1) = a_{11}{}^2(f_1 , f_1) = 1,$$

whence

$$b_{11} = 1/a_{11} = (f_1 , f_1)^{\frac{1}{2}}, \qquad \varphi_1 = \pm(f_1 , f_1)^{-\frac{1}{2}}f_1 .$$

Suppose that the functions φ_k $(k < n)$ satisfying 1)–3) have already been determined. Then f_n may be written as

$$f_n = b_{n1}\varphi_1 + \cdots + b_{n,n-1}\varphi_{n-1} + h_n,$$

where $(h_n, \varphi_k) = 0$ $(k < n)$.

Obviously, $(h_n, h_n) > 0$ [the assumption that $(h_n, h_n) = 0$ would contradict the linear independence of the set (6)].

Set

$$\varphi_n = (h_n, h_n)^{-\frac{1}{2}} h_n.$$

Then

$$(\varphi_n, \varphi_i) = 0 \qquad\qquad (i < n),$$

$$(\varphi_n, \varphi_n) = 1,$$

$$f_n = b_{n1}\varphi_1 + \cdots + b_{nn}\varphi_n \quad [b_{nn} = (h_n, h_n)^{\frac{1}{2}} \neq 0],$$

that is, the functions $\varphi_n(x)$ satisfy the conditions of the theorem. The last assertion of the theorem is an immediate consequence of the linear independence of the set $f_1, \cdots, f_n$.

The transition from a set (6) to the set (7) satisfying 1)–3) is called an *orthogonalization process*.

Obviously,

$$M(f_1, \cdots, f_n, \cdots) = M(\varphi_1, \cdots, \varphi_n, \cdots);$$

hence, the sets (6) and (7) are either both complete or not complete.

Therefore, the set (6) may be replaced by the set (7) in all problems of approximating functions f by linear combinations of the functions (6).

We said above that the existence in L_2 of a countable dense set implies the existence of a countable complete set of linearly independent functions. Orthogonalization of the latter set yields a complete countable orthonormal set.

EXERCISES

1. With the notation of the theorem in this section,

$$f_n = b_{n1}\varphi_1 + \cdots + b_{nn}\varphi_n.$$

Show that

$$b_{ni} = (f_n, \varphi_i) \qquad\qquad (1 \leq i \leq n).$$

2. Show that the set of functions

$$1, x, \cdots, x^n, \cdots$$

is linearly independent on any interval $[a, b]$.

3. For $R = [0, 1]$ and μ linear Lebesgue measure, show that $L_2(R, \mu)$ is infinite-dimensional.

4. Suppose that $\{f_1(x), \cdots, f_n(x)\} \subset L_2$. The Grammian of $\{f_i\}$ is the determinant

$$G_n = \det (f_i, f_j) \qquad (1 \le i, j \le n).$$

Show that $\{f_i\}$ is linearly dependent if, and only if, $G_n = 0$. Hints: Suppose $\{f_i\}$ is linearly dependent. Multiply the dependency relation by f_i $(1 \le i \le n)$ and integrate to obtain a system of homogeneous equations with a nontrivial solution. Conversely, if $G_n = 0$, then the same system has a nontrivial solution $a_1, \cdots, a_n$. Show that $(\sum_i a_i f_i, \sum_i a_i f_i) = 0$.

5. a) Show that the Legendre functions $P_n(x)$ given in the text form an orthogonal set.

b) Show that $\| P_n(x) \| = 2^{\frac{1}{2}}(2n + 1)^{-\frac{1}{2}}$. Hint: P_n is a polynomial of degree n. Use integration by parts repeatedly to show that $P_n(x)$ is orthogonal to x^k $(0 \le k < n)$.

§54. Fourier series over orthogonal sets. The Riesz-Fisher theorem

If $e_1, e_2, \cdots, e_n$ is an orthonormal base in Euclidean n-space $R^{(n)}$, then every vector $x \in R^{(n)}$ can be written in the form

(1) $$x = \sum_{k=1}^n c_k e_k,$$

with

$$c_k = (x, e_k).$$

The purpose of this section is, in a sense, to generalize (1) to the infinite-dimensional case.

Let

(2) $$\varphi_1, \cdots, \varphi_n, \cdots$$

be an orthonormal set and suppose that $f \in L_2$.

We pose the following problem: For prescribed n determine the coefficients α_k $(1 \le k \le n)$ so that the distance, in the sense of the metric in L_2, between f and the sum

(3) $$S_n = \sum_{k=1}^n \alpha_k \varphi_k$$

is the least possible.

Set $c_k = (f, \varphi_k)$. Since the set (2) is orthonormal,

(4) $$\| f - S_n \|^2 = (f - \sum_{k=1}^n \alpha_k \varphi_k, f - \sum_{k=1}^n \alpha_k \varphi_k)$$

$$= (f, f) - 2(f, \sum_{k=1}^n \alpha_k \varphi_k) + (\sum_{k=1}^n \alpha_k \varphi_k, \sum_{j=1}^n \alpha_j \varphi_j)$$

$$= \|f\|^2 - 2\sum_{k=1}^{n} \alpha_k c_k + \sum_{k=1}^{n} \alpha_k^2$$

$$= \|f\|^2 - \sum_{k=1}^{n} c_k^2 + \sum_{k=1}^{n} (\alpha_k - c_k)^2.$$

It is clear that the minimum of (4) is assumed when the last term is zero, i.e., if

(5) $$\alpha_k = c_k \qquad\qquad (1 \le k \le n).$$

In that case

(6) $$\|f - S_n\|^2 = (f, f) - \sum_{k=1}^{n} c_k^2.$$

DEFINITION. The numbers

$$c_k = (f, \varphi_k)$$

are called the *Fourier coefficients* of the function $f \in L_2$ relative to the orthonormal set (2), and the series

$$\sum_{k=1}^{\infty} c_k \varphi_k$$

(which may or may not converge) is called the *Fourier series* of the function f with respect to the set (2).

We have proved that of all the sums of the form (3) the partial sums of the Fourier series of the function deviate least (in the sense of the metric in L_2), for prescribed n, from the function f. The geometric meaning of this result may be explained as follows: The functions

$$f - \sum_{k=1}^{n} \alpha_k \varphi_k$$

are orthogonal to all the linear combinations of the form

$$\sum_{k=1}^{n} \beta_k \varphi_k ,$$

that is, these functions are orthogonal to the subspace generated by the functions $\varphi_1, \cdots, \varphi_n$ if, and only if, (5) is satisfied. (Verify this!) Hence, our result is a generalization of the well known theorem of elementary geometry which states that the length of the perpendicular from a given point to a line or a plane is less than that of any other line from the point to the given line or plane.

Since $\|f - S_n\|^2 \ge 0$, relation (4) implies that

$$\sum_{k=1}^{n} c_k^2 \le \|f\|^2,$$

where n is arbitrary and the right side is independent of n. Hence, the series $\sum_{k=1}^{\infty} c_k^2$ converges, and

(7) $$\sum_{k=1}^{\infty} c_k^2 \le \|f\|^2.$$

This is the *Bessel inequality*.

We introduce the following important

DEFINITION. An orthonormal set is said to be *closed* (sometimes *complete*) if

$$(8) \qquad \sum_{k=1}^{\infty} c_k^2 = \| f \|^2$$

for every $f \in L_2$. The relation (8) is called *Parseval's equality.*

It is clear from (6) that the set (2) is closed if, and only if, the partial sums of the Fourier series of every function $f \in L_2$ converge to f in the metric of L_2 (that is, in the mean).

The notion of a closed orthonormal set is intimately related to the completeness of a set of functions (see §53).

THEOREM 1. *In L_2 every complete orthonormal set is closed, and conversely.*

Proof. Suppose that $\{\varphi_n(x)\}$ is closed; then the sequence of partial sums of the Fourier series of every $f \in L_2$ is mean convergent. Hence the linear combinations of the elements of the set $\{\varphi_n(x)\}$ are dense in L_2 , that is, $\{\varphi_n\}$ is complete. Conversely, suppose that $\{\varphi_n\}$ is complete, that is, that every $f \in L_2$ can be approximated with arbitrary accuracy (in the sense of the metric in L_2) by linear combinations

$$\sum_{k=1}^{n} a_k \varphi_k$$

of elements of the set $\{\varphi_k\}$; then the partial sums

$$\sum_{k=1}^{n} c_k \varphi_k$$

of the Fourier series of f yield, in general, a still better approximation of f. Consequently, the series

$$\sum_{k=1}^{\infty} c_k \varphi_k$$

converges to f in the mean, and Parseval's equality holds.

In §53 we proved the existence of a complete orthonormal set in L_2 . Inasmuch as closure and completeness are equivalent for orthonormal sets in L_2 , the existence of closed orthonormal sets in L_2 need not be proved, and the examples of complete orthonormal sets in §53 are also examples of closed sets.

Bessel's inequality (7) implies that in order that numbers $c_1 , c_2 , \cdots$ be the Fourier coefficients of a function $f \in L_2$ with respect to an orthonormal set it is necessary that the series

$$\sum_{k=1}^{\infty} c_k^2$$

converge. In fact, this condition is not only necessary, but also sufficient. This result is stated in

THEOREM 2. (THE RIESZ-FISHER THEOREM.) *Let $\{\varphi_n\}$ be an arbitrary orthonormal set in L_2 , and let the numbers*

$$c_1 , \cdots , c_n , \cdots$$

be such that the series

(9) $$\sum_{k=1}^{\infty} c_k^{\,2}$$

converges. Then there exists a function $f \in L_2$ *such that*

$$c_k = (f, \varphi_k),$$

and

$$\sum_{k=1}^{\infty} c_k^{\,2} = (f, f).$$

Proof. Set

$$f_n = \sum_{k=1}^{n} c_k \varphi_k .$$

Then

$$\| f_{n+p} - f_n \|^2 = \| c_{n+1}\varphi_{n+1} + \cdots + c_{n+p}\,\varphi_{n+p} \|^2 = \sum_{k=n+1}^{n+p} c_k^{\,2}.$$

Since the series (9) converges, it follows, in view of the completeness of L_2 , that the sequence $\{f_n\}$ converges in the mean to a function $f \in L_2$. Furthermore,

(10) $$(f, \varphi_i) = (f_n , \varphi_i) + (f - f_n , \varphi_i),$$

where the first term on the right is equal to c_i $(n \geq i)$, and the second term approaches zero as $n \to \infty$, since

$$|(f - f_n , \varphi_i)| \leq \| f - f_n \| \cdot \| \varphi_i \|.$$

The left side of (10) is independent of n; hence, passing to the limit as $n \to \infty$, we obtain

$$(f, \varphi_i) = c_i .$$

Since, according to the definition of $f(x)$,

$$\| f - f_n \| \to 0 \qquad\qquad (n \to \infty),$$

it follows that

$$\sum_{k=1}^{\infty} c_k^{\,2} = (f, f).$$

This proves the theorem.

In conclusion, we prove the following useful theorem:

THEOREM 3. *In order that an orthonormal set of functions* (2) *be complete it is necessary and sufficient that there not exist in* L_2 *a function not equivalent to* $\psi \equiv 0$ *which is orthogonal to all the functions of* (2).

Proof. Suppose that the set (2) is complete, and hence closed. If $f \in L_2$

is orthogonal to all the functions of (2), then all its Fourier coefficients are equal to zero. Then Parseval's equality implies that

$$(f, f) = \sum c_k^2 = 0,$$

that is, $f(x)$ is equivalent to $\psi(x) \equiv 0$.

Conversely, suppose that $\{f_n\}$ is not complete, that is, there exists a function $g \in L_2$ such that

$$(g, g) > \sum_{k=1}^{\infty} c_k^2 \qquad\qquad [c_k = (g, \varphi_k)].$$

Then, by the Riesz-Fisher theorem, there exists a function $f \in L_2$ such that

$$(f, \varphi_k) = c_k, \qquad (f, f) = \sum_{k=1}^{\infty} c_k^2.$$

The function $f - g$ is orthogonal to all the functions φ_i. In view of the inequality

$$(f, f) = \sum_{k=1}^{\infty} c_k^2 < (g, g),$$

$f - g$ cannot be equivalent to $\psi(x) \equiv 0$. This proves the theorem.

EXERCISES

1. Let $\{\varphi_n(x)\}$ be an orthonormal set in L_2 and suppose $f \in L_2$. Verify that $f - \sum_{k=1}^{n} a_k \varphi_k$ is orthogonal to all linear combinations $\sum_{k=1}^{n} b_k \varphi_k$ if, and only if, $a_k = (f, \varphi_k)$ $(1 \le k \le n)$.

2. Let $\{\varphi_n(x)\}$ be an orthonormal set in L_2 and let $F \subseteq L_2$ be dense in L_2. If Parseval's equality holds for each $f \in F$, then it holds for all $g \in L_2$, i.e., $\{\varphi_n(x)\}$ is closed.

This may be proved as follows: Let $s_n(f) = \sum_{k=1}^{n} c_k \varphi_k(x)$ be the nth partial sum of the Fourier series of $f \in L_2$.

a) If $f, g \in L_2$, then

$$\| s_n(f - g) \| = \| s_n(f) - s_n(g) \| \le \| f - g \|.$$

b) Parseval's equality holds for g if, and only if,

$$\lim_{n \to \infty} \| g - s_n(g) \| = 0.$$

c) Now use the hypothesis of the exercise.

3. Let $\{\varphi_n(x)\}$, $\{\psi_n(x)\}$ be complete orthonormal sets in $L_2(R, \mu)$. Let $\mu^2 = \mu \otimes \mu$ and consider $L_2(R \times R, \mu^2)$.

a) The set $\{\chi_{nm}(x, y) = \varphi_n(x)\psi_m(y) : n, m = 1, 2, \cdots\}$ is orthonormal in $L_2(R \times R, \mu^2)$.

b) The set $\{\chi_{nm}(x, y)\}$ is complete.

Hint: Use Fubini's theorem and the criterion of Theorem 3 for completeness.

§55. Isomorphism of the spaces L_2 and l_2

The Riesz-Fisher theorem immediately implies the following important
THEOREM. *The space L_2 is isomorphic to the space l_2.*

[Two Euclidean spaces R and R' are said to be *isomorphic* if there is a one-to-one correspondence between their elements such that

$$x \leftrightarrow x', \qquad y \leftrightarrow y'$$

implies that
1) $x + y \leftrightarrow x' + y'$,
2) $\alpha x \leftrightarrow \alpha x'$,
3) $(x, y) \leftrightarrow (x', y')$.

Obviously, two isomorphic Euclidean spaces, considered merely as metric spaces, are isometric.]

Proof. Choose an arbitrary complete orthonormal set $\{\varphi_n\}$ in L_2 and assign to each function $f \in L_2$ the sequence $c_1, \cdots, c_n, \cdots$ of its Fourier coefficients with respect to this set. Since $\sum c_k^2 < \infty$, $(c_1, \cdots, c_n, \cdots)$ is an element of l_2. Conversely, in view of the Riesz-Fisher theorem, for every element $(c_1, \cdots, c_n, \cdots)$ of l_2 there is an $f \in L_2$ whose Fourier coefficients are $c_1, \cdots, c_n, \cdots$. This correspondence between the elements of L_2 and l_2 is one-to-one. Furthermore, if

$$f^{(1)} \leftrightarrow (c_1^{(1)}, \cdots, c_n^{(1)}, \cdots)$$

and

$$f^{(2)} \leftrightarrow (c_1^{(2)}, \cdots, c_n^{(2)}, \cdots),$$

then

$$f^{(1)} + f^{(2)} \leftrightarrow (c_1^{(1)} + c_1^{(2)}, \cdots, c_n^{(1)} + c_n^{(2)}, \cdots)$$

and

$$kf^{(1)} \leftrightarrow (kc_1^{(1)}, \cdots, kc_n^{(1)}, \cdots),$$

that is, addition and multiplication by scalars are preserved by the correspondence. In view of Parseval's equality it follows that

(1) $$(f^{(1)}, f^{(2)}) = \sum_{n=1}^{\infty} c_n^{(1)} c_n^{(2)}.$$

For, the relations

$$(f^{(1)}, f^{(1)}) = \sum (c_n^{(1)})^2, \qquad (f^{(2)}, f^{(2)}) = \sum (c_n^{(2)})^2$$

and

$$(f^{(1)} + f^{(2)}, f^{(1)} + f^{(2)}) = (f^{(1)}, f^{(1)}) + 2(f^{(1)}, f^{(2)}) + (f^{(2)}, f^{(2)})$$
$$= \sum (c_n^{(1)} + c_n^{(2)})^2$$
$$= \sum (c_n^{(1)})^2 + 2 \sum c_n^{(1)} c_n^{(2)} + \sum (c_n^{(2)})^2$$

imply (1). Hence the above correspondence between the elements of L_2 and l_2 is an isomorphism. This proves the theorem.

On the basis of this theorem we may regard l_2 as a "coordinate form" of L_2. It enables us to carry over to L_2 results previously established for l_2. For instance, we proved in Chapter III that every linear functional in l_2 is of the form

$$\varphi(x) = (x, y),$$

where y is an element of l_2 uniquely determined by the functional φ. In view of this and the isomorphism between L_2 and l_2, it follows that every functional in L_2 is of the form

$$\varphi(f) = (f, g) = \int f(x)g(x)\, d\mu,$$

where $g(x)$ is a fixed function of L_2. We proved in §24 that $\bar{l}_2 = l_2$. Hence $\bar{L}_2 = L_2$.

The isomorphism between L_2 and l_2 established above is closely related to the theory of quantum mechanics. Quantum mechanics originally consisted of two superficially distinct theories: Heisenberg's matrix mechanics and Schrödinger's wave mechanics. Schrödinger later showed that these two theories are equivalent. From the mathematical point of view, the difference between the two theories reduced to the fact that the Heisenberg theory used the space l_2, while the Schrödinger theory used the space L_2.

EXERCISES

1. Let $\{\varphi_n(x)\}$ be an orthonormal set in L_2. Then nonequivalent functions f, g have distinct Fourier series, i.e., for some n, $(f, \varphi_n) \neq (g, \varphi_n)$ if, and only if, $\{\varphi_n\}$ is complete. This result justifies the statement in the text that $f \leftrightarrow (c_1, c_2, \cdots, c_n, \cdots)$ is a one-to-one correspondence. Hint: Apply Theorem 3 of §54.

2. Let $\{\varphi_n\}$ be a complete orthonormal set in $L_2(R, \mu)$ and suppose $f \in L_2$. The Fourier series of $f(x)$ can be integrated term by term over an arbitrary measurable subset A of R, i.e.,

$$\int_A f(x)\, d\mu = \sum_{k=1}^{\infty} c_k \int_A \varphi_k(x)\, d\mu,$$

where $c_k = (f, \varphi_k)$ is the kth Fourier coefficient of $f(x)$.

Hint: Let $f^{(1)} = f$, $f^{(2)} = \chi_A$ in equation (1) of the theorem of this section.

Chapter IX

ABSTRACT HILBERT SPACE. INTEGRAL EQUATIONS WITH SYMMETRIC KERNEL

In the preceding chapter we proved that a separable L_2 is isomorphic with l_2, i.e., that they are two essentially different realizations of the same space. This space, usually called Hilbert space, plays an important part in analysis and its applications. It is often convenient not to restrict oneself, as previously, to various realizations of Hilbert space, but to define it axiomatically, for instance, as Euclidean n-space is defined in linear algebra.

§56. Abstract Hilbert space

DEFINITION 1. A set H of arbitrary elements $f, g, \cdots, h, \cdots$ is called an (abstract) Hilbert space if:

I. H is a linear space.

II. An inner product is defined in H, i.e., every pair of elements f, g is assigned a real number (f, g) such that

1) $(f, g) = (g, f)$,
2) $(\alpha f, g) = \alpha(f, g)$,
3) $(f_1 + f_2, g) = (f_1, g) + (f_2, g)$,
4) $(f, f) > 0$ if $f \neq 0$.

In other words, Conditions I and II mean that H is a Euclidean space. The number $\| f \| = (f, f)^{\frac{1}{2}}$ is called the *norm* of f.

III. The space H is complete in the metric $\rho(f, g) = \| f - g \|$.

IV. H is infinite-dimensional, that is, for every natural number n, H contains n linearly independent vectors.

V. H is separable. (This condition is often omitted; H may then be nonseparable.) Then H contains a countable dense set.

It is easy to give examples of spaces satisfying all the axioms. One such is the space l_2 discussed in Chapter II. In fact, l_2 is an infinite-dimensional Euclidean space, since the elements

$$e_1 = (1, 0, 0, \cdots, 0, \cdots)$$

$$e_2 = (0, 1, 0, \cdots, 0, \cdots)$$

$$e_3 = (0, 0, 1, \cdots, 0, \cdots)$$

$$\cdots\cdots\cdots\cdots\cdots\cdots$$

are linearly independent; it was proved in §§9 and 13 of Chapter II that it is complete and separable. The space L_2 of functions square integrable with respect to a separable measure, which is isomorphic to l_2, also satisfies the same axioms.

The following proposition holds:

All Hilbert spaces are isomorphic.

To prove this, it is obviously sufficient to show that every Hilbert space is isomorphic to the coordinate space l_2. The latter assertion is proved by essentially the same arguments as were used in the proof of the isomorphism of L_2 and l_2 :

1. The definitions of orthogonality, closure and completeness, which were introduced in §53 for elements of L_2, can be transferred unchanged to abstract Hilbert space.

2. Choosing in H a countable dense set and applying to it the process of orthogonalization described (for L_2) in §53, we construct in H a complete orthonormal set, that is, a set

$$(1) \qquad\qquad h_1 , \cdots , h_n , \cdots$$

satisfying:

a)

$$(h_i , h_k) = \begin{cases} 0 & (i \neq k), \\ 1 & (i = k). \end{cases}$$

b) The linear combinations of the elements of (1) are dense in H.

3. Let f be an arbitrary element of H. Set $c_k = (f, h_k)$. Then the series $\sum c_k^2$ converges, and $\sum c_k^2 = (f, f)$ for an arbitrary complete orthonormal set $\{h_k\}$ and $f \in H$.

4. Suppose again that $\{h_k\}$ is a complete orthonormal set in H. If

$$c_1 , \cdots , c_n , \cdots$$

is a sequence of numbers such that

$$\sum c_k^2 < \infty,$$

there exists an $f \in H$ such that

$$c_k = (f, h_k),$$

and

$$\sum c_k^2 = (f, f).$$

5. It is clear from what we have said that an isomorphism between H and l_2 can be realized by setting

$$f \leftrightarrow (c_1 , \cdots , c_n , \cdots),$$

where

$$c_k = (f, h_k)$$

and

$$h_1 , h_2 , \cdots, h_n , \cdots$$

is an arbitrary complete orthonormal set in H.

The reader may carry out the details of the proof as in §§53–55.

EXERCISES

1. a) The norm $\| f \|$ in H satisfies the parallelogram law:

$$\| f_1 + f_2 \|^2 + \| f_1 - f_2 \|^2 = 2(\| f_1 \|^2 + \| f_2 \|^2).$$

b) Conversely, if X is a complete separable normed linear space in which the norm satisfies the parallelogram law, then an inner product may be defined in X by

$$(f, g) = \tfrac{1}{4}[\| f + g \|^2 - \| f - g \|^2].$$

Moreover, $(f, f) = \| f \|^2$ and X becomes a Hilbert space. Hints: (i) Establish first that (x, y) is a continuous function of x. (ii) Show by induction that $(nx, y) = n(x, y)$. It will then readily follow that $(ax, y) = a(x, y)$. (iii) Then establish that $(x_1 + x_2 , y) = (x_1 , y) + (x_2 , y)$. The other properties of an inner product are immediate.

2. Suppose that $A \subseteq H$ has the property that $f, g \in A$ implies that $\tfrac{1}{2}(f + g) \in A$ (this is true, in particular, if A is convex). Let

$$d = \inf \{ \| f \| : f \in A\}.$$

If $\{f_n\} \subset A$ has the property that $\lim_{n \to \infty} \| f_n \| = d$, show that $\{f_n\}$ is a fundamental sequence in H.

Since H is complete, it follows that $\lim_{n \to \infty} f_n = f$ exists in H. If A is closed, then $f \in A$.

Hint: The parallelogram law yields

$$\| \tfrac{1}{2}(f_n - f_m)\|^2 = \tfrac{1}{2} \| f_n \|^2 + \tfrac{1}{2} \| f_m \|^2 - \| \tfrac{1}{2}(f_n + f_m) \|^2$$
$$\leq \tfrac{1}{2} \| f_n \|^2 + \tfrac{1}{2} \| f_m \|^2 - d^2.$$

3. In Def. 2 of §50 it is stated that the Schwarz inequality:

$$(f, g)^2 \leq \| f \|^2 \| g \|^2$$

holds. The author proves Schwarz's inequality in several concrete cases (see vol. 1, pp. 17, 18). Prove that the inequality holds in H (only Axioms I and II of §56 are required).

Hint: Suppose that $f, g \in H$ and that t is real. The quadratic polynomial with real coefficients in t: $(f + t(f, g)g, f + t(f, g)g)$ is nonnegative; hence, its discriminant must be nonpositive.

4. The inner product (f, g) is a continuous function of f and g, i.e., if $\| f_n - f \| \to 0$ and $\| g_n - g \| \to 0$ for $\{f_n\}$, $\{g_n\}$, f, g in H, then $(f_n, g_n) \to (f, g)$.

5. The following is an example of a nonseparable Hilbert space. Let H be the collection of all real-valued functions defined on $[0, 1]$ with $f(x) \neq 0$ for only countably many $x \in [0, 1]$, and such that if $f(x_n) \neq 0$ for $\{x_n\}$, then $\sum [f(x_n)]^2 < \infty$. The addition of functions and multiplication by real numbers is defined in the usual way, i.e., pointwise.

a) Define (f, g) analogously to the scalar product in l_2 and show that H satisfies I, II, III, IV in Def. 1.

b) Show that H is not separable. Hint: Show that H contains uncountably many disjoint open spheres.

6. If in the preceding example we restrict the collection H further to those $f(x)$ whose values are not zero for only finitely many x, then with the same operations H is also an incomplete metric space. That is, find a fundamental sequence in H whose limit is not in H. Note that the limit of such a sequence will be an element of H in Ex. 5.

§57. Subspaces. Orthogonal complements. Direct sums

In accordance with the general definitions of Chapter III, §21, a *linear manifold* in H is a subset L of H such that if f, $g \in L$, then $\alpha f + \beta g \in L$ for arbitrary numbers α and β. A *subspace* of H is a closed linear manifold in H.

We give several examples of subspaces of H.

1. Suppose that $h \in H$ is arbitrary. The set of all $f \in H$ orthogonal to h is a subspace of H.

2. Let $H = l_2$, that is, all the elements of H are sequences

$$(x_1, \cdots, x_n, \cdots)$$

of numbers such that $\sum x_k^2 < \infty$. The elements satisfying the condition $x_1 = x_2$ form a subspace.

3. Let H be the space L_2 of all square summable functions on a closed interval $[a, b]$ and suppose that $a < c < b$. We denote by H_c the collection of all functions of H identically zero on $[a, c]$. H_c is a subspace of H. If $c_1 < c_2$, then $H_{c_1} \supset H_{c_2}$, and $H_a = H$, $H_b = (0)$. Hence we obtain a continuum of subspaces of H ordered by inclusion. Each of these subspaces (with the exception, of course, of H_b) is infinite-dimensional and isomorphic to H.

The verification of the fact that each of the sets described in 1–3 is indeed a subspace of H is left to the reader.

Every subspace of a Hilbert space is either a finite-dimensional Euclidean space or itself a Hilbert space. For, Axioms I–III are obviously satisfied by a subspace and the validity of Axiom V follows from the following lemma:

LEMMA. *If a metric space R contains a countable dense set, every subspace R' of R contains a countable dense set.*

Proof. [TRANS. NOTE. The proof in the original was incorrect. We have therefore substituted the following proof.]

We assume that $R' \neq \emptyset$, otherwise there is nothing to prove.

Let $\{\xi_n\}$ be dense in R. For every pair of natural numbers n, k choose a $\zeta_{nk} \in R'$ (if it exists) such that

$$\rho(\xi_n, \zeta_{nk}) < 1/2k.$$

Then $\{\zeta_{nk} ; n, k = 1, 2, \cdots\}$ is dense in R'. To see this, suppose that $x \in R'$ and $\epsilon > 0$. Choose an s such that $1/s < \epsilon$. Since $\{\xi_n\}$ is dense in R and $x \in R$, there is an m such that $\rho(\xi_m, x) < 1/2s$. Hence ζ_{ms} exists and

$$\rho(x, \zeta_{ms}) \leq \rho(x, \xi_m) + \rho(\xi_m, \zeta_{ms}) < 1/2s + 1/2s = 1/s < \epsilon.$$

The existence in Hilbert space of an inner product and the notion of orthogonality enable us to supplement substantially the results of Vol. 1 on subspaces of arbitrary Banach spaces.

By orthogonalizing a countable dense sequence of elements of an arbitrary subspace of a Hilbert space, we obtain

THEOREM 1. *Every subspace M of H contains an orthogonal set $\{\varphi_n\}$ whose linear closure coincides with M:*

$$M = \bar{M}(\varphi_1, \cdots, \varphi_n, \cdots).$$

Let M be a subspace of H. Denote by

$$M' = H \ominus M$$

the set of $g \in H$ orthogonal to all $f \in M$. We shall prove that M' is also a subspace of H. The linearity of M' is obvious, since $(g_1, f) = (g_2, f) = 0$ implies that $(\alpha_1 g_1 + \alpha_2 g_2, f) = 0$. To prove closure, suppose that $g_n \in M'$ and that g_n converges to g. Then

$$(g, f) = \lim_{n \to \infty} (g_n, f) = 0$$

for all $f \in M$, and consequently $g \in M'$.

M' is called the *orthogonal complement* of M.

From Theorem 1 it easily follows that:

THEOREM 2. *If M is a subspace of H, every $f \in H$ is uniquely representable in the form $f = h + h'$, where $h \in M$, $h' \in M'$.*

Proof. We shall first prove the existence of the decomposition. To this end, we choose in M a complete orthonormal set $\{\varphi_n\}$ such that $M = \bar{M}\{\varphi_n\}$ and set

$$h = \sum_{n=1}^{\infty} c_n \varphi_n, \qquad c_n = (f, \varphi_n).$$

Since $\sum c_n{}^2$ converges (by the Bessel inequality), h exists and is an element of M. Set

$$h' = f - h.$$

Obviously,

$$(h', \varphi_n) = 0$$

for all n. Inasmuch as an arbitrary element ζ of M can be written as

$$\zeta = \sum a_n \varphi_n \,,$$

we have

$$(h', \zeta) = \sum_{n=1}^{\infty} a_n (h', \varphi_n) = 0.$$

We now suppose that, in addition to the above decomposition $f = h + h'$, there is another one:

$$f = h_1 + h_1', \qquad\qquad (h_1 \in M, h_1' \in M').$$

Then

$$(h_1, \varphi_n) = (f, \varphi_n) = c_n \,.$$

It follows that

$$h_1 = h, \qquad h_1' = h'.$$

Theorem 2 implies

COROLLARY 1. *The orthogonal complement of the orthogonal complement of a subspace M coincides with M.*

It is thus possible to speak of complementary subspaces of H. If M and M' are two complementary subspaces and $\{\varphi_n\}$, $\{\varphi_n'\}$ are complete orthonormal sets in M and M', respectively, the union of the sets $\{\varphi_n\}$ and $\{\varphi_n'\}$ is a complete orthonormal set in H. Therefore,

COROLLARY 2. *Every orthonormal set $\{\varphi_n\}$ can be extended to a set complete in H.*

If the set $\{\varphi_n\}$ is finite, the number of its terms is the dimension of M and also the deficiency of M'. Hence

COROLLARY 3. *The orthogonal complement of a subspace of finite dimension n has deficiency n, and conversely.*

If every vector $f \in H$ is represented in the form $f = h + h'$, $h \in M$, $h' \in M'$ (M' the orthogonal complement of M), we say that H is the *direct sum* of the orthogonal subspaces M and M' and write

$$H = M \oplus M'.$$

It is clear that the notion of a direct sum can be immediately generalized to an arbitrary finite or even countable number of subspaces: H is the direct sum of subspaces $M_1, \cdots, M_n, \cdots$:

$$H = M_1 \oplus \cdots \oplus M_n \oplus \cdots$$

if

1) the subspaces M_i are pairwise orthogonal, that is, an arbitrary vector in M_i is orthogonal to an arbitrary vector in M_k $(i \neq k)$;

2) every $f \in H$ can be written in the form

$$(1) \qquad\qquad f = h_1 + \cdots + h_n + \cdots \qquad\qquad (h_n \in M_n),$$

where $\sum \| h_n \|^2$ converges if the number of subspaces M_n is infinite.

It is easily verified that the sum (1) is unique and that

$$\| f \|^2 = \sum_n \| h_n \|^2.$$

A notion related to the direct sum of subspaces is that of the direct sum of a finite or countable number of arbitrary Hilbert spaces. If H_1, H_2 are Hilbert spaces, their direct sum H is defined as follows: the elements of H are all possible pairs (h_1, h_2), where $h_1 \in H_1$, $h_2 \in H_2$, and the inner product of two such pairs is

$$((h_1, h_2), (h_1', h_2')) = (h_1, h_1') + (h_2, h_2').$$

The space H obviously contains the orthogonal subspaces consisting of pairs of the form $(h_1, 0)$ and $(0, h_2)$, respectively; the first can be identified in a natural way with the space H_1, and the second with H_2.

The sum of an arbitrary finite number of spaces is defined in the same way. The sum $H = \sum_n \oplus H_n$ of a countable number of spaces $H_1, \cdots, H_n, \cdots$ is defined as follows: the elements of H are all possible sequences of the form

$$h = (h_1, \cdots, h_n, \cdots)$$

such that

$$\sum_n \| h_n \|^2 < \infty.$$

The inner product (h, g) of $h, g \in H$ is equal to

$$\sum_n (h_n, g_n).$$

EXERCISES

1. Prove Corollary 1 of Theorem 2.

2. Prove the remark before Corollary 2: If M, M' are complementary subspaces and if $\{\varphi_n\}$, $\{\varphi_n'\}$ are complete orthonormal sets in M, M', respectively, then their union is a complete orthonormal set in H.

3. If M, N are orthogonal subspaces, then

$$M + N = \{f + g : f \in M, g \in N\}$$

is closed, and therefore a subspace. If M, N are not orthogonal, the result need not be true. (An example can be found in Halmos, P. R., *Introduction to Hilbert Space and the Theory of Spectral Multiplicity*, New York, 1951.)

Hint: It is enough to show that if $\{f_n + g_n\}$ is a fundamental sequence, then $\{f_n\}$ and $\{g_n\}$ are also fundamental.

It is the purpose of the following exercises to extend some of the results of the text to general (i.e., nonseparable) Hilbert spaces.

4. If a subspace M of H is proper, i.e., $H \setminus M \neq \emptyset$, then there exists an element g of H, $g \neq 0$, such that g is orthogonal to every element of M.

Hint: For $h \in H \setminus M$, $h - M = \{h - x : x \in M\}$ is closed and convex. Let $d = \inf \{\| h - x \| : x \in M\}$, $d = \| h - x_0 \|$, $x_0 \in M$ (see §56, Ex. 2). For arbitrary real c and $f \in M$, show that

$$0 \leq \| h - (x_0 + cf) \|^2 - \| h - x_0 \|^2.$$

Show that this holds only if $g = h - x_0$ is orthogonal to M. g will be the required element.

5. If M, N are subspaces of H, $N \subseteq M$, then we denote by $M \ominus N$ the orthogonal complement of N in M (consider M itself as a Hilbert space). Show that $M = N \oplus (M \ominus N)$.

Hint: Let $L = N \oplus (M \ominus N)$, with $L \subseteq M$ and L closed (see Ex. 3). If L is properly contained in M, apply the result of Ex. 4 to obtain a contradiction.

6. Let $F(f)$ be a bounded linear functional on H. There exists one and only one element g in H such that $F(f) = (f, g)$ for every f in H [compare with equation (1) at the beginning of the next section].

a) The uniqueness is easy to establish.

b) Let $M = \{f : F(f) = 0\}$. M is a subspace. If $M = H$, choose $g = 0$. Otherwise, by Ex. 4 there exists an $h \neq 0$ such that h is orthogonal to M. Show that $g = [F(h)/(h, h)]h$ will do.

§58. Linear and bilinear functionals in Hilbert space

The isomorphism of every Hilbert space with l_2 enables us to carry over to an abstract Hilbert space the results established in Chapter III for l_2. Since every linear functional in l_2 is of the form

$$\varphi(x) = (x, a) \qquad (a \in l_2),$$

it follows that:

An arbitrary linear functional $F(h)$ in H is of the form

(1) $$F(h) = (h, g),$$

where g depends only on F.

Hence, the definition of weak convergence introduced in Chapter III for an arbitrary linear space, when applied to H can be stated in the following way:

A sequence $h_n \in H$ is weakly convergent to $h \in H$ if
1) the norms $\| h_n \|$ are bounded (see p. 90 of vol. 1);
2) for every $g \in H$,

$$(h_n, g) \to (h, g).$$

Ex. 4 at the end of the section shows that 2) implies 1).
An arbitrary orthonormal sequence

$$\varphi_1, \cdots, \varphi_n, \cdots$$

in H converges weakly to zero, since

$$c_n = (h, \varphi_n) \to 0 \qquad\qquad (n \to \infty)$$

for arbitrary $h \in H$, in view of the fact that

$$\sum c_n^2 \le (h, h) < \infty.$$

Such a sequence, of course, does not converge in the norm.

In particular, applying these remarks to the case when H is the space of square integrable functions on a closed interval $[a, b]$ of the real line with the usual Lebesgue measure, we obtain the following interesting result: Let

$$\varphi_1(t), \cdots, \varphi_n(t), \cdots$$

be an orthonormal set of functions in H, and let

$$f(t) = \begin{cases} 1 & (\text{on } [t_1, t_2] \subset [a, b]), \\ 0 & (\text{outside } [t_1, t_2]). \end{cases}$$

Then

$$(f, \varphi_n) = \int_{t_1}^{t_2} \varphi_n(t)\, dt.$$

Hence

$$\int_{t_1}^{t_2} \varphi_n(t)\, dt \to 0$$

for an arbitrary orthonormal set of functions $\varphi_n(t)$ and arbitrary t_1, $t_2 \in [a, b]$.

If the $\varphi_n(t)$ are uniformly bounded,

$$\int_a^b \varphi_n^2(t)\, dt = 1$$

only if the number of sign changes of $\varphi_n(t)$ on $[a, b]$ is unbounded as $n \to \infty$ (the same is to be observed, for instance, in the case of trigonometric functions).

In Chapter III, parallel with the concept of weak convergence of the elements of a linear normed space, we introduced the notion of weak convergence of a sequence of functionals. Inasmuch as Hilbert space coincides with its conjugate space, these two types of convergence are identical. Therefore, Theorem 1′ of §28 yields the following result for Hilbert space H:

The unit sphere in H is weakly compact, that is, every sequence $\varphi_n \in H$, with $\| \varphi_n \| \leq 1$, contains a weakly convergent subsequence.

In the sequel we require in addition the following

THEOREM 1. *If ξ_n is weakly convergent to ξ in H, then*

$$\| \xi \| \leq \sup \| \xi_n \|.$$

Proof. For every complete orthonormal set $\{\varphi_k\}$ in H,

$$c_k = (\xi, \varphi_k) = \lim_{n \to \infty} (\xi_n, \varphi_k) = \lim_{n \to \infty} c_{nk},$$

$$\sum_{m=1}^{k} c_m{}^2 = \lim_{n \to \infty} \sum_{m=1}^{k} c_{nm}{}^2 \leq \sup_n \sum_{m=1}^{\infty} c_{nm}{}^2;$$

consequently,

$$\sum_{m=1}^{\infty} c_m{}^2 \leq \sup_n \sum_{m=1}^{\infty} c_{nm}{}^2,$$

which proves the theorem.

Let $B(f, g)$ be a real-valued function of pairs of elements of H satisfying the following condition: $B(f, g)$ is a linear functional of f for fixed g, and a linear functional of g for fixed f. $B(f, g)$ is called a *bilinear functional*. A bilinear functional $B(f, g)$ is said to be *symmetric* if

$$B(f, g) = B(g, f) \qquad\qquad (f, g \in H).$$

The theorem on the general form of a linear functional in H implies that every bilinear functional in H can be written in the form

$$B(f, g) = (\zeta, g),$$

where ζ depends on f. It is easily seen that the correspondence

$$f \to \zeta$$

is a continuous linear operator in H; denote it by A. Hence

(2) $$B(f, g) = (Af, g).$$

An alternative form

$$B(f, g) = (f, A^*g),$$

where A^* is the adjoint operator of A, can be obtained in a similar fashion. [In Chapter III, in considering linear operators on an arbitrary Banach space E, we defined the adjoint operator A^* of A by means of the relation

$$(Ax, \varphi) = (x, A^*\varphi) \qquad (x \in E, \varphi \in \bar{E}).$$

If E is a Hilbert space, then $\bar{E} = E$, and the definition of A^* in Chapter III reduces to the definition given above.] If a functional $B(f, g)$ is symmetric, then

$$(Af, g) = B(f, g) = B(g, f) = (Ag, f) = (f, Ag),$$

that is,

$$(3) \qquad\qquad A = A^*.$$

A linear operator satisfying (3) is said to be *self-adjoint*.

Formula (2) defines a one-to-one correspondence between the bilinear functionals and the continuous linear operators on H, with the symmetric bilinear functionals corresponding to the self-adjoint linear operators, and conversely.

Setting $f = g$ in a symmetric bilinear functional, we obtain a *quadratic functional*

$$Q(f) = B(f, f).$$

According to (2),

$$Q(f) = (Af, f),$$

where A is a self-adjoint linear operator.

Since the correspondence between the symmetric bilinear functionals and the quadratic functionals is one-to-one $[Q(f) = B(f, f)$, and conversely: $B(f, g) = \frac{1}{4}\{Q(f + g) - Q(f - g)\}]$, the correspondence between the quadratic functionals and the self-adjoint linear operators is also one-to-one.

EXERCISES

1. Let M be a proper subspace of H, $F(h)$ a (bounded) linear functional on M with norm $\| F \|$. Then there exists a linear functional F^* on H such that $F^*(h) = F(h)$ for $h \in M$ and $\| F^* \| = \| F \|$. (See vol. 1, p. 86, the Hahn-Banach theorem.) Hint: Apply equation (1) at the beginning of this section to the Hilbert space M.

2. a) Let $\{f_n\}$ and $f(x)$ belong to H. If $\{f_n\}$ converges strongly to f, then $\{f_n\}$ converges weakly to f.

   b) The converse is false. Show that for $L_2(R, \mu)$, where $R = [0, 1]$ and μ is linear Lebesgue measure, that $\{\sin nx\}$ is weakly convergent to

$f(x) \equiv 0$, but $\{\sin nx\}$ is not fundamental in the norm; hence it cannot converge strongly to any element of L_2.

c) The following partial converse is true. If $\{f_n\}$ converges weakly to f and $\| f_n \|$ converges to $\| f \|$, then $\{f_n\}$ converges strongly to f. Hint: Show that $(f - f_n, f - f_n) \to 0$.

3. Suppose $A \subseteq H$. If A is weakly closed, then A is a norm closed subset of H. More explicitly: Suppose $\{f_n\} \subset A$ and $(f_n, g) \to (f, g)$ for every $g \in H$ implies that $f \in A$. Show that $\| f_n - f \| \to 0$ and $\{f_n\} \subset A$ implies $f \in A$.

4. The definition of weak convergence of $\{h_n\}$ to h in H lists two conditions. We propose to show that the second condition already implies the first. This result in a more general setting is known as the Banach-Steinhaus theorem.

a) It is enough to show that there exists a constant $M > 0$ and a sphere $S = \{g : \| g - g_0 \| \leq r\}$ such that $g \in S$ implies $| (h_n, g) | \leq M$. For if this implication holds and $\| g \| \leq r$, then

$$| (h_n, g) | = | (h_n, g + g_0) - (h_n, g_0) | \leq 2M.$$

Now show that $g \in H$ implies

$$| (h_n, g) | \leq (2M/r) \| g \|$$

and consequently

$$\| h_n \| \leq 2M/r.$$

b) It follows that if the result is false, the sequence $\{| (h_n, g) |\}$ must be unbounded in every sphere, i.e., given $a > 0$ and S a sphere in H, there is an element $g_a \in S$ and an index n_a for which $| (h_{n_a}, g_a) | > a$. Show by continuity of (h, g) in the second argument that S contains a closed sphere S_a such that $g \in S_a$ implies $| (h_{n_a}, g) | > a$.

c) Now construct by induction a sequence of closed spheres $\{S_k\}$ and a sequence $\{n_k\}$ such that $S_k \subseteq S_{k-1}$; diam $S_k \leq 1/k$; $n_1 < n_2 < \cdots < n_k < \cdots$; $n_k \to \infty$ and $| (h_{n_k}, g) | > k$ for $g \in S_k$.

d) Use the completeness of the metric space H to show the existence of a point g_0 for which $| (h_{n_k}, g_0) | > k$. This contradicts Condition 2): $(h_n, g_0) \to (h, g_0)$.

5. Let M_1 and M_2 be two subspaces with M_1 a proper subset of M_2. Show that there exists an element g of M_2 such that $\| g \| = 1$ and $\| g - f \| \geq 1$ for any $f \in M_1$. Hint: Consider M_2 as a Hilbert space with subspace M_1.

6. a) Let X be a Banach space, M a subspace of X and $\bar{x} = M + x = \{y + x : y \in M\}$ a subset of X defined for each $x \in X$. We can make the collection $\{\bar{x} : x \in X\} = X/M$ into a vector space, called the *quotient space*

of X mod M by defining $\bar{x} + \bar{y} = \{M + (x + y)\}$ and $a\bar{x} = \{M + ax\}$. Verify that the operations are uniquely defined and that X/M is a vector space with zero element $\bar{0} = M$.

b) A norm is introduced by defining

$$\| \bar{x} \| = \inf \{ \| y + x \| : y \in M \}.$$

Show that X/M is a normed linear space. The fact that M is closed is required to show that $\| \bar{x} \| = 0$ if, and only if, $\bar{x} = \bar{0}$.

c) It is also true that X/M is complete, i.e., X/M is a Banach space. This is more difficult to prove.

7. If $X = H$ and M is a subspace of H, show that H/M and $H \ominus M$ are isomorphic normed vector spaces. In other words, suppose that $f \in H$, $f = h + h'$, with $h \in M$, $h' \in M'$. Suppose that $\bar{f}$ corresponds to h' and show that this correspondence is one-to-one, onto and preserves addition, multiplication by scalars, and the norm. Hint: $\| f \|^2 = \| h \|^2 + \| h' \|^2$.

§59. Completely continuous self-adjoint operators in H

In Chapter IV we introduced the notion of a completely continuous linear operator, acting on a Banach space E. In this section we restrict the discussion to self-adjoint completely continuous operators acting on a Hilbert space, supplemented by the results already established for arbitrary completely continuous operators.

We recall that we called an operator A completely continuous if it mapped every bounded set into a compact set. Inasmuch as $H = \bar{H}$, that is, H is conjugate to a separable space, the bounded sets in H are precisely the weakly compact sets (see Ex. 1 at the end of the section). Therefore, the definition of a completely continuous operator on a Hilbert space can be stated as follows:

An operator A acting on a Hilbert space H is said to be completely continuous if it maps every weakly compact set into a compact set (relative to the norm).

In a Hilbert space this is equivalent to the condition that the operator A map every weakly convergent sequence into a norm convergent sequence (see Ex. 2 at the end of the section).

In this section we shall prove the following fundamental theorem, a generalization to completely continuous operators of the theorem on the reduction of the matrix of a self-adjoint linear transformation in n-dimensional space to diagonal form:

THEOREM 1. *For every completely continuous self-adjoint linear operator A on a Hilbert space H there exists an orthonormal set of eigenvectors (characteristic vectors; see vol. 1, p. 110) $\{\varphi_n\}$, corresponding to eigenvalues (characteristic* *values*) $\{\lambda_n\}$, *such that every* $\xi \in H$ *can be written uniquely in the form* $\xi = \sum_k c_k\varphi_k + \xi'$, *where the vector* ξ' *satisfies the condition* $A\xi' = 0$. *Also*

$$A\xi = \sum_k \lambda_k c_k \varphi_k ,$$

and $\lim_{n\to\infty} \lambda_n = 0$.

For the proof of this fundamental theorem we require the following lemmas:

LEMMA 1. *If* $\{\xi_n\}$ *converges weakly to* ξ *and the self-adjoint linear operator* A *is completely continuous, then*

$$Q(\xi_n) = (A\xi_n , \xi_n) \to (A\xi, \xi) = Q(\xi).$$

Proof.

$$| (A\xi_n , \xi_n) - (A\xi, \xi) | \leq | (A\xi_n , \xi_n) - (A\xi_n , \xi) + (A\xi_n , \xi) - (A\xi, \xi) |.$$

But

$$| (A\xi_n , \xi_n) - (A\xi_n , \xi) | = | (\xi_n , A(\xi_n - \xi)) | \leq \| \xi_n \| \cdot \| A(\xi_n - \xi) \|$$

and

$$| (A\xi_n , \xi) - (A\xi, \xi) | = | (\xi, A(\xi_n - \xi)) | \leq \| \xi \| \cdot \| A(\xi_n - \xi) \|.$$

Since the numbers $\| \xi_n \|$ are bounded and $\| A(\xi_n - \xi) \| \to 0$,

$$| (A\xi_n , \xi_n) - (A\xi, \xi) | \to 0.$$

This proves the lemma.

LEMMA 2. *If a functional*

$$| Q(\xi) | = | (A\xi, \xi) |,$$

where A *is a bounded self-adjoint linear operator, assumes a maximum at a point* ξ_0 *of the unit sphere, then*

$$(\xi_0 , \eta) = 0$$

implies that

$$(A\xi_0 , \eta) = (\xi_0 , A\eta) = 0.$$

Proof. Obviously, $\| \xi_0 \| = 1$. Set

$$\xi = (\xi_0 + a\eta)/(1 + a^2 \| \eta \|^2)^{\frac{1}{2}},$$

where a is an arbitrary number. From $\| \xi_0 \| = 1$ it follows that

$$\| \xi \| = 1.$$

Since

$$Q(\xi) = (1 + a^2 \| \eta \|^2)^{-1}[Q(\xi_0) + 2a(A\xi_0 , \eta) + a^2Q(\eta)],$$

it follows that

$$Q(\xi) = Q(\xi_0) + 2a(A\xi_0, \eta) + O(a^2)$$

for small values of a. It is clear from the last relation that if $(A\xi_0, \eta) \neq 0$, then a can be chosen so that $|Q(\xi)| > |Q(\xi_0)|$. This contradicts the hypothesis of the lemma.

It follows immediately from Lemma 2 that if $|Q(\xi)|$ assumes a maximum at $\xi = \xi_0$, then ξ_0 is an eigenvector of the operator A.

Proof of the theorem. We shall construct the elements φ_k by induction, in the order of decreasing absolute values of the corresponding eigenvalues:

$$|\lambda_1| \geq \cdots \geq |\lambda_n| \geq \cdots .$$

To construct the element φ_1 we consider the expression $Q(\xi) = |(A\xi, \xi)|$ and show that it assumes a maximum on the unit sphere. Let

$$S = \sup \{|(A\xi, \xi)|; \|\xi\| \leq 1\}$$

and suppose that $\xi_1, \xi_2, \cdots$ is a sequence such that $\|\xi_n\| \leq 1$ and

$$|(A\xi_n, \xi_n)| \rightarrow S \qquad\qquad (n \rightarrow \infty).$$

Since the unit sphere in H is weakly compact, $\{\xi_n\}$ contains a subsequence weakly convergent to an element η. In view of Theorem 1, §58, $\|\eta\| \leq 1$, and by Lemma 1,

$$|(A\eta, \eta)| = S.$$

We take η as φ_1. Clearly, $\|\eta\| = 1$. Also

$$A\varphi_1 = \lambda_1\varphi_1,$$

whence

$$|\lambda_1| = |(A\varphi_1, \varphi_1)|/(\varphi_1, \varphi_1) = |(A\varphi_1, \varphi_1)| = S.$$

Now suppose that the eigenvectors

$$\varphi_1, \cdots, \varphi_n$$

corresponding to the eigenvalues

$$\lambda_1, \cdots, \lambda_n$$

have already been constructed. We consider the functional

$$|(A\xi, \xi)|$$

on the elements of

$$M_n' = H \ominus M(\varphi_1, \cdots, \varphi_n)$$

(that is, the set orthogonal to $\varphi_1, \cdots, \varphi_n$) and such that $\| \xi \| \leq 1$. $M_n{}'$ is an invariant subspace (a subspace which is mapped into itself) of A [since $M(\varphi_1, \cdots, \varphi_n)$ is invariant and A is self-adjoint]. Applying the above arguments to M_n, we obtain an eigenvector φ_{n+1} of A in $M_n{}'$.

Two cases are possible: 1) after a finite number of steps we obtain a subspace $M_{n_0}{}'$ in which $(A\xi, \xi) \equiv 0$; 2) $(A\xi, \xi) \not\equiv 0$ on $M_n{}'$ for all n.

In the first case Lemma 2 implies that A maps $M_{n_0}{}'$ into zero, that is, $M_{n_0}{}'$ consists of the eigenvectors corresponding to $\lambda = 0$. The set of vectors $\{\varphi_n\}$ is finite.

In the second case we obtain a sequence $\{\varphi_n\}$ of eigenvectors for each of which $\lambda_n \neq 0$. We show that $\lambda_n \to 0$. The sequence $\{\varphi_n\}$ (like every orthonormal sequence) is weakly convergent to zero. Therefore, $A\varphi_n = \lambda_n\varphi_n$ converge to zero in the norm, whence $| \lambda_n | = \| A\varphi_n \| \to 0$.

Let

$$M' = H \ominus M\{\varphi_n\} = \bigcap_n M_n{}' \neq 0.$$

If $\xi \in M'$ and $\xi \neq 0$, then

$$(A\xi, \xi) \leq | \lambda_n | \| \xi \|^2$$

for all n, that is,

$$(A\xi, \xi) = 0.$$

Hence, applying Lemma 2 (for sup $\{| (A\xi, \xi) |; \| \xi \| \leq 1\} = 0$) to M', we obtain $A\xi = 0$, that is, A maps the subspace M' into zero.

From the construction of the set $\{\varphi_n\}$ it is clear that every vector can be written in the form

$$\xi = \sum_k c_k\varphi_k + \xi' \qquad\qquad (A\xi' = 0).$$

Hence

$$A\xi = \sum_k \lambda_k c_k\varphi_k.$$

EXERCISES

1. Let A be a continuous linear operator of H into H. Suppose that $\{f_n\} \subset H, f \in H$ and $\{f_n\}$ converges weakly to f. Show that $\{Af_n\}$ converges weakly to Af.

2. In the second paragraph of this section it is stated that in H the norm bounded sets are precisely the weakly compact sets. Show that this is true as follows:

a) If $A \subseteq H$ is norm bounded, i.e., there exists an $M > 0$ such that $\| f \| < M$ for all $f \in A$, then Theorem 1' of §28 (see vol. 1) shows that A is weakly compact (see the statement preceding Theorem 1 in §58).

b) If A is weakly compact, show that A is norm bounded. Use Ex. 4 of §58 for this purpose.

3. In the fourth paragraph of this section it is stated that the following two properties of an operator A on H are equivalent:

a) A maps every weakly compact set into a norm compact set.

b) A maps every weakly convergent sequence into a norm convergent sequence.

Prove that a) and b) are equivalent.

4. Let A be a continuous (bounded) linear operator of H into H with the additional property that $A(H)$, the range of A, is contained in a finite-dimensional subspace of H. Then A is completely continuous. Hint: The Bolzano-Weierstrass theorem holds in E_n .

5. Let A be a completely continuous operator, $T = I - A$ and suppose $M \subseteq H$, $M = \{x : Tx = 0\}$. Show that M is a finite-dimensional subspace of H.

§60. Linear equations in completely continuous operators

We consider the equation

$$(1) \qquad \xi = cA\xi + \eta,$$

where A is a completely continuous self-adjoint operator, $\eta \in H$ is prescribed and $\xi \in H$ is the unknown.

Let

$$\varphi_1, \cdots, \varphi_n, \cdots$$

be the eigenvectors of A corresponding to the eigenvalues different from zero. Then η can be written as

$$(2) \qquad \eta = \sum_n a_n \varphi_n + \eta',$$

where $A\eta' = 0$. We shall seek a solution of (1) of the form

$$(3) \qquad \xi = \sum_n x_n \varphi_n + \xi',$$

where $A\xi' = 0$. Substitution of (2) and (3) into (1) yields

$$\sum_n x_n(1 - \lambda_n c)\varphi_n + \xi' = \sum_n a_n \varphi_n + \eta'.$$

This equation is satisfied if, and only if,

$$\xi' = \eta',$$

$$x_n(1 - \lambda_n c) = a_n ,$$

that is, if

$$\xi' = \eta',$$

$$(4) \qquad\qquad x_n = a_n/(1 - \lambda_n c) \qquad\qquad (\lambda_n \neq 1/c),$$

$$a_n = 0 \qquad\qquad (\lambda_n = 1/c).$$

The last equality gives a necessary and sufficient condition for a solution of (1), and (4) determines the solution. The values of x_n corresponding to those n for which $\lambda_n = 1/c$ remain arbitrary.

§61. Integral equations with symmetric kernel

The results presented in the preceding section can be applied to integral equations with symmetric kernel, that is, to equations of the form

$$(1) \qquad\qquad f(t) = \varphi(t) + \int_a^b K(t, s) f(s) \, ds,$$

where $K(t, s)$ satisfies the conditions

1) $K(t, s) = K(s, t)$,

2) $\displaystyle\int_a^b \int_a^b K^2(t, s) \, dt \, ds < \infty.$

The application of the results of §60 to equations of the form (1) is based on the following theorem:

THEOREM. *Let R be a space with measure μ. If a function $K(t, s)$ defined on $R^2 = R \times R$ satisfies the conditions*

$$(2) \qquad\qquad K(t, s) = K(s, t)$$

and

$$(3) \qquad\qquad \int_{R^2} K^2(t, s) \, d\mu^2 < \infty \qquad\qquad (\mu^2 = \mu \otimes \mu),$$

then the operator

$$g = Af$$

defined on $L_2(R, \mu)$ by the formula

$$g(t) = \int_R K(t, s) f(s) \, d\mu_s$$

is completely continuous and self-adjoint.

Proof. We shall denote the space $L_2(R, \mu)$ simply by L_2. Let $\{\psi_n(t)\}$ be a complete orthonormal set in L_2. The collection of all possible products $\psi_n(t)\psi_m(s)$ is a complete orthonormal set of functions in R^2 (see Ex. 3, §54), and

$$(4) \qquad\qquad K(t, s) = \sum_m \sum_n a_{mn} \psi_n(t) \psi_m(s)$$

in the mean [i.e., $\sum_m \sum_n$ converges to K in the norm of $L_2(R^2, \mu^2)$], where

$$a_{mn} = a_{nm}$$

(in view of (2)), and

$$\sum_m \sum_n a_{mn}^2 = \int_{R^2} K^2(t, s) \, d\mu^2 < \infty.$$

We set

(5) $$f(s) = \sum_n b_n \psi_n(s)$$

in the mean. Then

(6) $$g(x) = (Af)(x) = \sum_m \left(\sum_n a_{mn} b_n\right) \psi_m(x) = \sum_m c_m \psi_m(x)$$

in the mean. Also

$$c_m^2 = \left(\sum_{n=1}^{\infty} a_{mn} b_n\right)^2 \leq \sum_{n=1}^{\infty} a_{mn}^2 \cdot \sum_{n=1}^{\infty} b_n^2 = \| f \|^2 \cdot a_m^2,$$

where

$$a_m^2 = \sum_n a_{mn}^2.$$

Since the series

$$\sum_{m=1}^{\infty} a_m^2 = \sum_m \sum_n a_{mn}^2$$

converges, for every $\epsilon > 0$ there is an m_0 such that

$$\sum_{m=m_0+1}^{\infty} a_m^2 < \epsilon,$$

(7)

$$\| g(x) - \sum_{m=1}^{m_0} c_m \psi_m(x) \|^2 = \sum_{m=m_0+1}^{\infty} c_m^2 < \epsilon \| f \|^2.$$

Now suppose that $\{f^{(k)}\}$ is weakly convergent to f. Then the corresponding $c_m^{(k)}$ converge to c_m for every m. Hence the sum

$$\sum_{m=1}^{m_0} c_m^{(k)} \psi_m(x)$$

converges in the mean to the sum

$$\sum_{m=1}^{m_0} c_m \psi_m(x)$$

for arbitrary fixed m_0. In view of the inequality (7) and the boundedness of the norm $\| f^{(k)} \|$ it follows that $\{g^{(k)}(x)\}$ (where $g^{(k)} = Af^{(k)}$) converges in the mean to $g(x)$. This proves that A is completely continuous. Multiplying (4) by (5), integrating with respect to μ_t and comparing the result with (6), we see that

$$(Af)(s) = \int_R K(s, t) f(t) \, d\mu_t.$$

This and Fubini's theorem imply that

$$(Af, g) = \int_R \left(\int_R K(s, t) f(t) \ d\mu_t \cdot g(s) \right) d\mu_s$$

$$= \int_R f(t) \left(\int_R K(s, t) g(s) \ d\mu_s \right) d\mu_t$$

$$= (f, Ag),$$

that is, A is self-adjoint. This proves the theorem.

Hence the solution of an integral equation with symmetric kernel satisfying conditions (2) and (3) reduces to finding the eigenfunctions and eigenvalues of the corresponding integral operator. The actual solution of the latter problem usually requires the use of some approximation method, but such methods are outside the scope of this book.

EXERCISES

1. Let $R = [a, b]$ be an interval on the real line, μ linear Lebesgue measure, $H = L_2(R, \mu)$, $K(t, s)$ as in the theorem of §61. Then by Theorem 1 of §59, the operator A determined by K has an orthonormal sequence of eigenfunctions $\{\varphi_n\}$ corresponding to a sequence $\{\lambda_n\}$ of eigenvalues $\lambda_n \neq 0$. Further, for $f(t) \in H$, $f(t) = \sum_{n=1}^{\infty} (f, \varphi_k) \varphi_k(t) + h(t)$ in the mean, with $Ah = 0$, i.e., $\int_R h(t) K(t, s) \ d\mu_s = 0$ and $g(s) = (Af)(s) = \sum_{k=1}^{\infty} \lambda_k (f, \varphi_k) \varphi_k(s)$ in the mean.

Suppose now that there is a constant M such that $\int_R |K(t, s)|^2 \ d\mu_s < M^2$ for all $t \in [a, b]$. An example is furnished by $K(t, s) = |t - s|^{-a}$, $a < \frac{1}{2}$.

Show that the series for $g(s)$ will converge uniformly and absolutely (pointwise) to $g(s)$.

Hints: For uniform convergence, apply the condition and Schwarz's inequality. For absolute convergence, show that mean convergence of a series with orthogonal terms is equivalent to convergence of the series with positive terms $(\sum_k \| \varphi_k \|^2)$ and that therefore the convergence is independent of the order of the terms.

SUPPLEMENT AND CORRECTIONS TO VOLUME 1

(1) p. 28, l. 23. Substitute $G_\alpha(x)$ for G_α .

(2) p. 46, l. 13* (l. 13 from bottom). Replace "the method of successive approximations is not applicable" by "the method of successive approximations is, in general, not applicable".

(3) p. 49, after l. 10* insert: "An arbitrary continuous function may be chosen for $f_0(x)$".

(4) p. 50, l. 1*. Replace the λ after the inequality sign by $|\lambda|$.

(5) p. 51, l. 2. Replace M by M^2.

p. 51, l. 3. Replace M by M^n (two times). Replace λ^n by $|\lambda|^n$ (two times).

p. 51, l. 5. Replace λ^n by $|\lambda|^n M^n$.

(6) p. 56, l. 6. Replace "closed region" by "closed bounded region".

p. 59, l. 2*. Replace the first occurrence of Y by X.

(7) p. 61, after l. 9 insert: "A mapping $y = f(x)$ is said to be *uniformly continuous* if for every $\epsilon > 0$ there is a $\delta > 0$ such that $\rho(f(x_1), f(x_2)) < \epsilon$ for all x_1 , x_2 for which $\rho(x_1 , x_2) < \delta$. The following theorem holds: *Every continuous mapping of a compactum into a compactum is uniformly continuous*. This theorem is proved in the same way as the uniform continuity of a function continuous on a closed interval".

(8) p. 61, l. 18. After "Proof" insert: "We shall prove the necessity first. If D is compact, D contains a finite $\epsilon/3$-chain $f_1 , \cdots , f_N$. Since each mapping f_i is continuous, it is uniformly continuous. Therefore, there is a $\delta > 0$ such that

$$\rho(f_i(x_1), f_i(x_2)) < \epsilon/3 \qquad (1 \leq i \leq n)$$

if

$$\rho(x_1 , x_2) < \delta.$$

If $f \in D$, there exists an f_i such that

$$\rho(f, f_i) < \epsilon/3.$$

Then

$$\rho(f(x_1), f(x_2)) \leq \rho(f(x_1), f_i(x_1)) + \rho(f_i(x_1), f_i(x_2))$$
$$+ \rho(f_i(x_2), f(x_2)) < \epsilon/3 + \epsilon/3 + \epsilon/3 = \epsilon$$

if $\rho(x_1 , x_2) < \delta$. But this means that the set of all $f \in D$ is equicontinuous. We shall now prove the sufficiency."

(9) p. 72, l. 3*. Replace "max" by "sup".

(10) p. 77, l. 9. Replace "continuous" by "continuous at a point x_0".

123

p. 77, l. 13. Replace $\| x_1 - x_2 \|$ by $\| x - x_0 \|$.

p. 77, l. 11. Replace $| f(x_1) - f(x_2) |$ by $| f(x) - f(x_0) |$.

p. 77, l. 20. Replace "continuous" by "uniformly continuous". Delete "everywhere in R".

(11) p. 80, l. 9*. Replace "$x_0 \notin L_f$" by "x_0 is a fixed element of the complement of L_f".

(12) p. 84, l. 12. Replace "$\sup_n x_n$" by "$\sup_n | x_n |$".

(13) p. 92, l. 14*, 13*. The assertion that the functionals δ_{t_0} generate a dense subset of $\bar{C}$ is not true. Replace "satisfies the conditions of Theorem 1, i.e. linear combinations of these functionals are everywhere dense in $\bar{C}_{[a,b]}$" by "has the property that if a sequence $\{x_n(t)\}$ is bounded and $\varphi(x_n) \to \varphi(x)$ for all $\varphi \in \Delta$, then $\{x_n(t)\}$ is weakly convergent to $x(t)$".

(14) p. 94, l. 9* ff. The metric introduced here leads to a convergence which is equivalent to the weak convergence of functionals in every bounded subset of $\bar{R}$ (but not in all of $\bar{R}$). In l. 6*, after "so that" insert "in every bounded subset of $\bar{R}$". On p. 95, l. 10, after "that" insert "for bounded sequences of $\bar{R}$".

(15) p. 116. The proof of Theorem 5 contains an error. It should be replaced by the following:

Proof. 1°. We note first that every nonvanishing eigenvalue of a completely continuous operator has finite multiplicity. In fact, the set E_λ of all eigenvectors corresponding to an eigenvalue λ is a linear subspace whose dimension is equal to the multiplicity of the eigenvalue. If this subspace were infinite-dimensional for some $\lambda \neq 0$, the operator A would not be completely continuous in E_λ, and hence would not be completely continuous in the whole space.

2°. Now to complete the proof of the theorem it remains to show that if $\{\lambda_n\}$ is a sequence of distinct eigenvalues of a completely continuous operator A, then $\lambda_n \to 0$ as $n \to \infty$. Let x_n be an eigenvector of A corresponding to the eigenvalue λ_n. The vectors x_n are linearly independent. Let E_n $(n = 1, 2, \cdots)$ be the subspace of all the elements of the form

$$y = \sum_{i=1}^{n} \alpha_i x_i .$$

For each $y \in E_n$,

$$y - \lambda_n^{-1} A y = \sum_{i=1}^{n} \alpha_i x_i - \sum_{i=1}^{n} \alpha_i \lambda_i \lambda_n^{-1} x_i = \sum_{i=1}^{n-1} (1 - \lambda_i \lambda_n^{-1}) \alpha_i x_i ,$$

whence it is clear that $y - \lambda_n^{-1} A y \in E_{n-1}$.

Choose a sequence $\{y_n\}$ such that

$$y_n \in E_n , \qquad \| y_n \| = 1, \qquad \rho(y_n , E_{n-1}) > \tfrac{1}{2}.$$

(The existence of such a sequence was proved on p. 118, l. 6 ff.)

We now suppose that the sequence $1/\lambda_n$ is bounded. Then the set $\{A(y_n/\lambda_n)\}$ is compact. But this is impossible, since

$$\| A(y_p/\lambda_p) - A(y_q/\lambda_q) \|$$
$$= \| y_p - [y_p - \lambda_p^{-1}Ay_p + A(y_q/\lambda_q)] \| > \tfrac{1}{2} \quad (p > q),$$

inasmuch as $y_p - \lambda_p^{-1}Ay_p + A(y_q/\lambda_q) \in E_{p-1}$. This contradiction proves the assertion.

(16) p. 119, l. 12. The assertion that G_0 is a subspace is true, but not obvious. Therefore the sentence "Let G_0 be the subspace consisting of all elements of the form $x - Ax$" should be replaced by the following: "Let G_0 be the linear manifold consisting of all elements of the form $x - Ax$. We shall show that G_0 is closed. Let $\tilde{T}$ be a one-to-one mapping of the quotient space E/N (where N is the subspace of the elements satisfying the condition $x - Ax = 0$) onto G_0. (For the definition of quotient space see Ex. 5, §57.) We must show that the inverse mapping $\tilde{T}^{-1}$ is continuous. It is sufficient to show that it is continuous at $y = 0$. Suppose that this is not so; then there exists a sequence $y_n \to 0$ such that $\| \xi_n \| \geq \rho > 0$, where $\xi_n = \tilde{T}^{-1}y_n$. Setting $\eta_n = \xi_n/\| \xi_n \|$ and $z_n = y_n/\| \xi_n \|$, we obtain a sequence $\{\eta_n\}$ satisfying the conditions:

$$\| \eta_n \| = 1, \qquad \tilde{T}\eta_n = z_n \to 0.$$

If we choose in each class η_n a representative x_n such that $\| x_n \| \leq 2$, we obtain a bounded sequence, and $z_n = Tx_n = x_n - Ax_n \to 0$. But since the operator A is completely continuous, $\{Ax_n\}$ contains a fundamental subsequence $\{Ax_{n_k}\}$. The sequence $x_p = z_p + Ax_p$ (where $x_p = x_{n_p}$ and $z_p = z_{n_p}$) is also fundamental and therefore converges to an element x_0. Hence $z_p = Tx_p \to Tx_0$, so that $Tx_0 = 0$, that is, $x_0 \in N$. But then $\| \eta_p \| \leq \| x_p - x_0 \| \to 0$, which contradicts the condition $\| \eta_p \| = 1$. This contradiction proves the continuity of $\tilde{T}^{-1}$ and shows that G_0 is closed. Hence G_0 is a subspace".

INDEX